Zero fighter

Martin Caidin

Zero fighter

BB

Editor-in-Chief: Barrie Pitt
Art Director: Peter Dunbar

Military Consultant: Sir Basil Liddell Hart
Picture Editor: Bobby Hunt

Executive Editor: David Mason
Art Editor: Sarah Kingham
Designers: Fry/Evans
Cover: Denis Piper
Research Assistant: Yvonne Marsh
Cartographer: Richard Natkiel
Special Drawings: John Batchelor

Ballantine Books Inc.
101 Fifth Avenue, New York, NY10003

Contents

Out of the sun
Introduction by Saburo Sakai

It is highly pleasing that Martin Caidin, one of the co-authors of my book SAMURAI!, has written a new book about the Zero fighter at a time when many nations are preparing to commemorate, in 1970, the 25th anniversary of the end of World War II.

The role played by Zero fighters in the Pacific War can scarcely be over-emphasized. As I look back on the war now with all that I have learned in the past twenty-four years, I am inclined to believe that the Zero's strength and performance, unparalleled in 1940 when it made its debut and throughout the early years of the war, was partly responsible for the outbreak of the war.

Had President Franklin D Roosevelt and Secretary of State Cordell Hull taken at face value US Intelligence appraisals of Zero fighters as they ranged over China in 1941, they would have hesitated in serving an ultimatum to Japan one month before Pearl Harbor. Historians point out that the ultimatum demanded, in substance, that Japan surrender unconditionally to the Allies without fighting. Japanese war leaders, who

fully appreciated the Zero fighter's value, elected to hit Pearl Harbor. Japan did surrender in 1945, after her country was devastated – but who gained from the war? I don't think that the United States gained anything from the costly war, when I look at many international events that have taken place in recent years.

If Roosevelt and Hull failed to appraise the value of the Zero correctly in · 1941, few other Americans knew anything about it at all. Later during the Pacific War, American war correspondents of course wrote stories about the Imperial Navy's wonder fighters; but their stories, like most other war stories written out of limited information for home consumption, lacked proper perspective and were not very accurate or comprehensive.

It was Martin Caidin who, in co-operation with his Japanese Navy friends and the Mitsubishi designer of the plane, wrote the first comprehensive book about this plane in 1956, and who later helped to write my book about my experiences in the war flying the Zero fighter. For these two books I believe Caidin will be remembered by

posterity as the man who gave the Zero fighter its proper place in history; therefore, I am pleased that this new book on the subject is authored by a man more qualified than any one else.

In fact, the Zero fighter's significance reaches beyond the historical role it played during the Pacific War. Its significance was also industrial: a combat plane of the first rank, it was indeed the crystalization of Japanese high precision technology, and the first manifestation of Japanese originality and ingenuity in the development of aircraft. In other words, the Zero fighter was a harbinger of what Japan would produce industrially three decades later.

Today, in an era of peace, the star airplane of Japan is the YS-11, a turbojet passenger plane of extremely high stability and very short take-off and landing lengths, which is already gaining popularity with the airlines of many foreign countries. Among the designers of the YS-11 was Jiro Horikoshi, who originated the Zero fighter. The achievement of Japan is especially remarkable because the Allied occupation of Japan from 1945 to 1952 broke up the Japanese aircraft industry and forbade its resuscitation: it was not revived in Japan until as late as 1960. Meanwhile, many Japanese aircraft engineers and technicians in the occupation days were forced to switch to automotive shops, the nation's automotive industry, thus started up from scratch, is now the world's second biggest, exceeded only by the United States, with four million units produced last year.

To those who know enough about the Zero fighter, Japan's industrial achievement today is not a wonder at all.

During the Allied occupation, all remaining Zero fighters were destroyed or taken away from Japan. Four years ago, however, Guam Island was kind enough to return one of these wartime Zeros to Japan. And I recently heard more exciting news. Canadian friends are going to wing a few well-maintained Zero fighters next year to Osaka for demonstration flights over Expo '70. I am looking forward to that occasion as much as I am to Caidin's new book.

Foretaste of the end

At 13,000 feet a solid overcast greyed out the Pacific sky. The men who formed the Japanese bastion of Iwo Jima, 650 miles to the south of Yokosuka, Japan, enjoyed their relief from the broiling sun. The nights had been filled with savage attacks by hundreds of American bombers. Now, with the sun obscured, the men felt grateful for the brief respite from the daily heat.

But the Japanese pilots, high overhead, were irritable. Few had slept the night before. The cascade of bombs through the long hours had forced them into dusty caves, the air choked with volcanic ash pounded upward by the thundering explosions. At 0520 hours on the 24th June 1944 the air raid sirens went off. Sentries hammered sticks against large pans – anything to create the loudest din possible. Less than sixty miles to the south, reported the men of the early-warning radar station, was a large force of American aircraft. They were closing fast. The Japanese pilots raced for their fighters, engines already started by the ground crews, and then dust swirled through the air as more than eighty Zero fighters raced down the runways, tucked up their gear, and arrowed into the grey sky.

There was one advantage to the overcast skies. Below the cloud deck there was no danger of the enemy diving out of the sun onto the helpless Japanese, blinded by the sun. But no one knew what might be found above the clouds, or if the enemy, coming in high, would make a diving attack. Japanese air to ground communications were poor at their best and the pilots knew they were on their own.

They also knew the Americans had gained an unwitting advantage. The Japanese radar determined the bearing and distance of the enemy force but not its height. If the full defending force of Zero fighters remained together to gain advantage of massed strength they might miss the incoming aircraft, and thus Iwo's defenses could be hit a shattering blow while the Zeros milled about uselessly.

Strength lay in numbers but the Japanese had no choice. Without spotter aircraft circling high over Iwo Jima they had to decide whether to meet the Americans above or

Japan's trump card, the Zero

8

The Zero's first conqueror, the US Navy's Grumman Hellcat

below the clouds, or both. The Zero pilots signalled to one another, and split their formation. Forty-two fighters pulled up into steep climbs and bored through the clouds. They burst into clear skies above. The Japanese pilots searched in every direction. Nothing. Except for themselves the sky was empty. Immediately the Zeros regrouped, edged into combat formation, the pilots preparing themselves for any contingency.

Barely in time for a fighter pilot's dream . . .

A loose swarm of American fighters climbed steeply from the clouds. As they climbed through the mists the American pilots had loosened their formations for safety. When they emerged from the dull-grey world of the clouds, the pilots blinked in the dazzling sunshine. Their formations were loose and, of far greater importance to the Japanese, the speed of the American fighters was low. Few Zero pilots paid much attention to

the fact that the American planes were the new Grumman F6F Hellcats, snub-nosed killers with performance greatly superior to that of the older Mitsubishi A5M series Zero fighters. The Japanese had the advantage of the moment, and there were enough experienced pilots, including several aces, not to lose the rare opportunity. Immediately the Zeros swept in to attack, diving swiftly against the American aircraft which had been caught momentarily, but fatally, off balance.

For several terrible seconds the Hellcats could offer no defense. Pilots rammed throttles forward in desperate attempts to gain speed, to turn into the Zeros diving cloudward in the classic bounce from out of the sun. Their speed low, noses up in a climb, caught unawares, blinded by the sun, the Hellcats could only take punishment until the Japanese swept through them.

Two Japanese pilots especially cracked the whip. Naval Air Pilot 1/C Kinsute Muto was the leading ace of the Yokosuka Wing. A scarred veteran of hundreds of air battles, he was an excellent shot and a superb pilot, who knew how to close in to point-blank range or to catch an enemy with a deflection burst at long range. Muto came down at full power, under perfect control. His guns and cannon hammered out sharp bursts at close range. Two Hellcats flamed almost immediately as the Japanese ace caught the enemy aircraft, sweeping from one victim to the other. He caught a third Hellcat as it dived away, the pilot rolling his aircraft in a frantic bid to escape the diving enemy. The third Hellcat took a long burst in its fuel tanks and exploded, but Muto was already hard after another fighter. The American pilot twisted and jinked beautifully. Against the average Japanese pilot he would have made good his escape, but Muto was anything but average. Cannon shells exploded in the Hellcat's cockpit and Muto registered his fourth kill of the brief mêlée.

His swift victories brought jubilant shouts from the other Zero pilots, who later confirmed the four kills. That jubilation overshadowed, for the moment, the fact that the remaining American fighters were diving for the clouds. Several took long bursts and damaging hits but survived the initial onslaught. The Hellcats tore into the protective clouds below, diving safely from nearly three miles high.

The Japanese had the advantage. Except for Kinsuke Muto they all wasted their chance.

The first indication the forty Japanese pilots waiting below the clouds had of the brief air battle far above was the sight of an American fighter twisting earthward with a long trail of greasy smoke showing thinly. Flame appeared, growing swiftly as the fighter increased its speed. Moments later a swarm of Hellcats knifed downward from the clouds, diving steeply, moving with great speed. The Americans caught sight of the Japanese almost at the same moment the Zero pilots reacted to the diving aircraft.

The Japanese had the advantage of a tight formation. They knew, also, that whatever had taken place above the clouds, the Zero pilots who had tangled with the Americans would be diving after their fleeing quarry.

It should have been an impressive advantage for the Japanese.

It was not, for several reasons.

By now, of course, the Americans were alert to any situation into which they might run. They were also moving with great speed, much greater, in fact, than the Zeros that rose to meet them in an organized wedge. There was another factor, invisible in terms of statistical compilation.

The average American pilot in the swirling fight was superior to his opponent. In the force above the clouds had been Kinsuke Muto. With the forty-odd pilots in the lower force was Saburo Sakai, one of Japan's greatest aces. Yet Sakai flew at a disadvantage. Grievously wounded long before this moment, he flew with sight in only one eye. He had not been in combat for years. Now, suddenly, he was thrust into a fierce air battle, with most of the Japanese pilots about him ill-trained and lacking experience against the Americans.

The Hellcat pilots suffered no such disadvantage. Caught unawares, they recovered swiftly. As they plunged through the clouds and caught sight of the enemy aircraft the American pilots rushed in at the Zeros.

'There was no hesitation on the part of the American pilots,' Saburo Sakai said of the huge air fight. 'The Grummans screamed in to attack. Then the planes were all over the sky, swirling from sea level to the cloud layer in wild dogfights. The formations were shredded . . . '

What took place in that great dogfight was determined as much by design philosophy and political bankruptcy as it was the measure of opposing pilots and aircraft. The long and short of it, in the summer of 1944, was that the Japanese were outclassed. Even had the contesting pilots been of equal skill the advantage had of necessity to lie with the Americans.

The Zero fighter defending Iwo Jima in 1944 was essentially the same aircraft that had fought in China four years earlier. It had been improved, to be sure. Its engine was more reliable and somewhat more powerful, and design changes had improved its

Above: Inferior in performance, but superior in ruggedness, the Grumman F4F Wildcat. *Below:* Shot out of the skies on nearly every occasion on which it met the Zero, the Brewster F2A Buffalo

performance and increased its cutting power as a weapon. It was a better aircraft than the Zero fighters that had ripped through the opposition of years before, slashing through the Tomahawks, Airacobras, Mohawks and Buffalos that had been its principal opposition. It was a better aircraft, but not all that much better. Its performance had been improved, but only relatively slightly.

In the early days of the war the Japanese Zero's chief opponent, the fighter mainstay of the American navy, was the Grumman F4F Wildcat. There had been some clashes with the Brewster F2A Buffalo but no-one would even dare to suggest that those were equal fights. The Zero so outclassed the Buffalo that such encounters were repetitious slaughters rather than combat.

The Wildcat was another story. The stubby Grumman was of equal power to the Zero, but its greater weight gave the Japanese aircraft the advantage in speed, rate of climb, acceleration, and maneuverability. The sturdiness of the Grumman was, unquestionably, one of its redeeming features but this could hardly be expected to give to the Wildcat pilots a clear advantage in a heated contest where flight performance must ultimately be the deciding factor of victory or defeat.

Good as the Wildcat was, it was not as good as the Zero. With pilots of equal skill in each plane the Zero inevitably must emerge the winner.

Now it was the summer of 1944. The situation had changed completely, but the Mitsubishi Zero had not. Essentially it was the same fighter that had fought in China and swept aside the opposition in battle from Burma to Pearl Harbor.

Over Iwo Jima the Zeros ran into the successor to the Wildcat. The new fighter, the Grumman F6F Hellcat, was a new breed.

Instead of the 1,200 horsepower engine of the Wildcat, its 'big brother' had the invaluable advantage of 2,000 horsepower. The new Hellcat was much faster than either the Wildcat or the Zero. Its .50-inch machine guns had several times the ammunition supply of older fighters. Compared with the Zero, the Hellcat was faster

in level flight, could climb faster and could outdive it. Its firepower and its gunsight were also superior.

There was another advantage that came as a shock to the Zero pilots.

Until the Zeros ran into the Hellcat, the Japanese fighter was the undisputed master in maneuverability of all the combatants in the vast Pacific area. That precious advantage vanished with the debut of the Hellcat.

The new American fighter, at high speed, still retained excellent roll control, unlike the Zero which, at high speeds, suffered from ailerons that stiffened and became extremely difficult to move. Many an American pilot had previously escaped an attacking Zero by diving at the greatest possible speed and rolling either left or right, knowing that the pursuing enemy aircraft would have difficulty following the maneuver. But at slower speeds, at the speeds with which most fighter pilots mixed it' with the enemy, the Zero had been the aircraft.

This was now no longer true, as the Japanese discovered to their dismay. For as the aircraft tore at one another in individual dogfights the Zero pilots found that their tight loops and steep, sucked-in turns no longer gave them the superiority on which they had always counted so strongly – the Hellcat could turn with the Zero.

At slow speeds the two fighters were matched evenly in turning ability. But the American fighter had better acceleration and rate of climb. At higher speeds the Hellcat proved even more maneuverable than the agile Japanese machine. Then, when there were added the advantages of greater firepower and superior construction, including armor plating and self-sealing fuel tanks in the Grumman, it was the Japanese pilot who found himself on the short end of the stick.

Before the savage, scattered air battle ended, perhaps as many as ten or twelve Hellcats were shot out of the sky, including the four machines gunned down by the swift Kinsuke Moto, as well as those that were shot down by Saburo Sakai. Lest the reader draw the erroneous conclusion that the air battle of 24th June 1944 over the island of Iwo Jima was a one-sided victory for the Japanese, it must be emphasized that these two pilots between them scored almost all the victories achieved by the defenders. Several other Hellcats fell to the more experienced Japanese pilots, but their number was all too few.

The Hellcat pilots shot down nearly forty enemy fighters, a victory ratio of approximately four to one in favor of the American naval fighters. Yet a truly great pilot can hold his own even against overwhelming odds and sometimes even emerge victorious. Such was the case with Saburo Sakai over Iwo Jima on that fateful summer day. The episode which follows, told by Sakai in his own words, reveals the superlative skill of this astonishing fighter pilot. One wonders what might have been the outcome had Sakai had at his disposal a fighting machine as good as the Hellcats he faced. For the Zero fighter, on which Japan had placed such momentous hopes at the beginning of the war, and which had led it to such smashing victories over much of the eastern hemisphere, was now the defender in a sky full of superior fighter aircraft.

Saburo Sakai takes us back to that moment after the opening combat above the clouds. The Hellcats plunged earthward and burst into view of the forty Japanese fighters waiting beneath the cloud deck. The planes broke formation, the fight was joined.

"I snapped into a tight loop and rolled out on the tail of a Hellcat, squeezing out a burst as soon as the plane came into the range finder. He rolled away and my bullets met only empty air. I went into a left vertical spiral, and kept closing the distance, trying for a clear shot at the plane's belly. The Grumman tried to match the turn with me; for just that moment I needed, his underside filled the range finder and I squeezed out a second burst. The cannon shells exploded along the fuselage. The next second thick clouds of black smoke poured back from the airplane and it went into a wild, uncontrolled dive for the sea.

Everywhere I looked there were fighters, long trails of smoke, bursts of flame, and exploding flames. I looked too long. Flashing tracers poured directly beneath my wing and instinctively I jerked the stick over to the left, rolling back to get on his tail and snapping out a burst. Missed. He dove out of range, faster than I could follow.

I cursed at myself for having been caught without warning, and with equal vehemence I cursed my blind eye, which left almost half of my area of vision blank. As quickly as I could I slipped out of the parachute straps and freed my body, so I could turn around in my seat, making up for the loss of side vision.

And I looked without a second to spare. At least a half-dozen Grummans were on my tail, jockeying into firing position. Their wings burst into sparkling flame as they opened fire. Another left roll – fast! – and the tracers slipped harmlessly by. The six fighters ripped past my wings and zoomed in climbing turns to the right.

Not this time! Oh, no! I slammed the throttle on overboost and rolled back to the right, turning after the six fighters with all the speed the Zero would give me. I glanced behind me – no other fighters in the back. One of these was going to be mine, I swore! The Zero closed the distance to the nearest plane rapidly. Fifty yards away I opened up with the cannon, watching the shells move up the fuselage and disappear into the cockpit. Bright flashes and smoke appeared beneath the glass; the next moment the Hellcat swerved crazily and fell off on one wing, its smoke trail growing with each second.

But there were more fighters on my tail! Suddenly I didn't want to close with them. Weariness spread over me like a smothering cloak. In the old days, at Lae, I would have wasted no time in hauling the Zero around and going for them. But now I felt as though my stamina had been wrung dry. I didn't want to fight.

I dove and ran for it. In this condition it would have been sheer suicide to oppose the Hellcats. A slip, a second's delay in moving the stick or the rudder bar . . . and that would be all. I wanted time in which to regain my breath, to shake off the sudden dizziness. Perhaps it was the result of trying to see as much with only one eye as I had before; I knew only that

I couldn't fight.

I fled to the north, using overboost to pull away. The Hellcats turned back and went after fresher game . . .

I circled slowly, north of Iwo, sucking in air and trying to relax. The dizziness left me, and I turned back to the battle area. The fight was over. There were still Zeros and Hellcats in the sky, but they were well separated, and the fighters of both sides were forming into their own groups.

Ahead and to the right I saw fifteen Zeros swinging into formation, and I closed in to join the group. I came up below the formation and . . .

Hellcats! Now I understood why the surgeon, long ago, had protested my return to combat so vigorously. With only one eye my perspective was badly off, the small details were lost to me in identifying planes at a distance. Not until the white stars against the blue wings became clear did I realize my error. I wasted no time in throwing off the fear which gripped me. I rolled to the left and came around in a tight turn, diving for speed, hoping the Grummans hadn't seen me.

No such luck. The Hellcat formation broke up and the planes turned in pursuit. What could I do? My chances seemed hopeless.

No – there was still one way out, and a slim chance at that. I was almost over Iwo Jima. If I could outmaneuver the other planes – an almost impossible task, I realized – until their fuel ran low and forced them to break for home . . .

Now I appreciated the speed of these new fighters. In seconds they were closing in. They were so fast! There was no use in running any further . . .

I snapped back in a tight turn. The maneuver startled the enemy pilots as I climbed at them from below, swinging into a spiral. I was surprised; they didn't scatter. The lead fighter responded with an equal spiral, matching my maneuver perfectly. Again I spiraled, drawing it closer this time. The opposing fighters refused to yield a foot.

This was something new. An Airacobra or a P-40 would have been lost trying to match me in this fashion, and not even the Wildcat could hold a spiral too long against the Zero. But these new Hellcats – they were the most maneuverable enemy planes I had ever encountered. I came out of the spiral into a trap. The fifteen fighters filed out of their spirals into a long column. And the next moment I found myself circling in the center of a giant ring of fifteen Grummans. On every side of me I saw the broad wings with their white stars. If ever a pilot was surrounded in the air, I was.

I had little time in which to ponder my misfortune. Four Grummans broke out of their circle and dove at me. They were too eager. I rolled easily out of the way and the Hellcats skidded by, out of control. But what I thought was only a slight roll set me up for several other fighters. A second quartet flashed out of the ring, right on my tail.

I ran. I gunned the engine to give every last ounce of power and pulled away sufficiently to get out of their gun range for the moment. The four pursuing planes didn't worry me; it was the first quartet. How right I was! They had climbed back from their skidding plunge and were above me, diving for another firing pass.

I slammed my right foot against the rudder bar, skidding the Zero to the left. Then the stick, hard over to the left, rolling sharply. Sparkling lights flashed beneath my right wing, followed by a plummeting Hellcat.

I came out of the roll in a tight turn. The second Grumman was about 700 yards behind me, its wings already enveloped in yellow flame from its guns. If I hadn't know it before, I knew it now. The enemy pilots were as green as my own inexperienced fliers . . . and that could be a factor which could save my life.

The second fighter kept closing in, spraying tracers all over the sky, tracers which fell short of my own plane. Keep it up! I yelled, keep it up! Go ahead, waste all your ammunition; you'll be one less to worry about. I turned again and fled, the Hellcat closing in rapidly. When he was about 300 yards behind, I rolled away to the left. The Grumman passed below me, still firing at empty air.

I lost my temper. Why run from such a clumsy pilot? Without thinking, I rolled back and got on his tail. From fifty yards away I snapped out a cannon burst.

Wasted. I failed to correct for the skid caused by my abrupt turn. And suddenly I didn't care what happened to the fighter in front of me ... another Grumman was on my tail, firing steadily. Again – the left roll, a maneuver which never failed me. The Hellcat roared past, followed by the third and fourth fighters in the quartet.

Another four planes were almost directly above me, ready to dive. Sometimes, you have to attack in order to defend yourself. I went into a vertical climb, directly beneath the four fighters. The pilots banked their wings back and forth, trying to find me. I had no time to scatter them. Three Hellcats came at me from the right. I narrowly missed their tracers as I evaded with the same left roll.

The fighters were back in their wide ring. Any move I made to escape would bring several Grummans cutting at me from different directions. I circled in the middle, looking for a way out.

They had no intention of allowing that to happen. One after the other, the fighters peeled off from the circle and came at me, firing as they closed in.

I cannot remember how many times the fighters attacked nor how many times I rolled away. The perspiration rolled down my body, soaking my underclothes. My forehead was all beads of sweat, and it began to drip down onto my face. I cursed when the salty liquid trickled into my left eye ... I couldn't take the time to rub it with my hand! All I could do was to blink, try to keep the salt away, try to see.

I was tiring much too quickly. I didn't know how I could get away from the ring. But it was very clear that these pilots weren't as good as their planes. An inner voice seemed to whisper to me. It repeated over an over the same words ... speed ... keep up your speed ... forget the engine, burn it out, keep up your speed! ... keep rolling ... never stop rolling ...

My arm was beginning to go numb from the constant rolling to the left to evade the Hellcats' tracers. If I

Saburo Sakai, grievously wounded but never defeated

once slackened my speed in flicking away to the left, it would be my end. But how long could I keep that necessary speed in rolling away?

I must keep rolling! As long as the Grummans wanted to keep their ring intact, only one fighter at a time could jump me. And I had no fear of evading any single plane as it made its firing pass. The tracers were close, but they must hit me exactly if they were going to shoot me down. It mattered not whether the bullets passed a hundred yards or a hundred inches away, just so long as I could evade them.

I needed time to keep away from the fighters which raced in, one after the other, peeling off from the wide ring they maintained about me.

I rolled. Full throttle.

Stick over to the left.

Here comes another!

Hard over. The sea and horizon spinning crazily.

Skid!

Another!

That was close!

Tracers. Bright. Shining. Flashing.

Always underneath the wing.

Stick over.

Keep your speed up!

Roll to the left.

Roll.

My arm! I can hardly feel it any more!

Had any of the Hellcat pilots chosen a different approach for his firing pass or concentrated carefully on his aim, I would surely have been shot out of the air. Not once did the enemy pilots aim at the point toward which my plane was moving. If only one fighter had spilled its tracers into the empty space leading me, toward the area where I rolled every time, I would have flown into his bullets.

But there is a peculiarity about fliers. Their psychology is strange, except for the rare few who stand out and go on to become leading aces. Ninety-nine per cent of all pilots adhere to the formula they were taught in school. Train them to follow a certain pattern and, come what may, they will never consider breaking away from that pattern when they are in a battle where life and death mingle with one another.

So this contest boiled down to

endurance between the time my arm gave out and I faltered in my evading roll and the fuel capacity of the Hellcats. They still had to fly back to their carriers.

I glanced at the airspeed indicator. Nearly 350 miles per hour. The best that the Zero could do.

I needed endurance for more than my arm. The fighter also had its limits. I feared for the wings. They were bending under the repeated violence of the evading roll maneuvers. There was a chance that the metal might collapse under continued pressure and the wing would tear off from the Zero, but that was out of my hands. I could only continue to fly. I must force the plane through the evasive rolls or die.

Roll.
Snap the stick over!
Skid.
Here comes another one.
To hell with the wings! Roll!
I could hear nothing. The sound of the Zero's engine, the roaring thunder of the Hellcats, the heavy staccato of their .50 caliber guns, all had disappeared.
My left eye stung.
The sweat streamed down.
I couldn't wipe it.
Watch out!
Stick over. Kick the bar.
There go the tracers. Missed again.

The altimeter was down to the bottom; the ocean was directly beneath my plane. Keep the wings up,

Sakai, you'll slap a wave with your wingtip. Where had the dogfight started? Thirteen thousand feet. More than two and a half miles of skidding and rolling away from the tracers, lower and lower. Now I had no altitude left.

But the Hellcats couldn't make their firing runs as they had before. They couldn't dive; there was no room to pull out. Now they would try something else. I had a few moments. I held the stick with my left hand, shook the right vigorously. It hurt. Everything hurt. Dull pain, creeping numbness.

Here they come, skidding out of their ring. They're careful now, afraid of what I might do suddenly.

Zero, once master of the sky

He's rolling. A rolling pass.

It's not so hard to get out of the way. Skid to the left. Look.

The tracers.

Fountains geysering up from the water. Spray. Foam.

Here comes another one.

How many times have they come at me this way now? I've lost count. When will they give up? They *must* be running low on fuel!

But I could no longer roll so effectively. My arms were going numb. I was losing my touch. Instead of coming about with a rapid, sharp rolling motion, the Zero arched around in a sloppy oval, stretching

out each maneuver. The Hellcats saw it. They pressed home their attacks, more daring now. Their passes came so fast that I had barely time for a breather.

I could no longer keep this up. I must take a break! I came out of another left roll, kicked the rudder bar and swung the stick over to the left. The Zero clawed around in response and I gunned the fighter for a break in the ring. I was out, nosing down again and running for it, right over the water. The Hellcats milled around for a moment in confusion. Then they were after me again.

Half the planes formed a barricade overhead, while the others, in a cluster of spitting guns, hurtled after me. The Hellcats were too fast. In a few seconds they were in firing range. Steadily I kept working to the right, kicking the Zero over so that she jerked hard with each maneuver. To the left fountains of white foam spouted into the air from the tracers which continued narrowly to miss my plane.

They refused to give up. Now the fighters overhead were coming down after me. The Grummans immediately behind snapped out their bursts, and the Hellcats which dove tried to anticipate my moves. I could hardly move my arms or legs. There was no way out. If I continued flying low, it would only be a matter of a minute or two before I moved the stick too slowly. Why wait to die, running like a coward?

I hauled the stick back, my hands almost in my stomach. The Zero screamed back and up, and there, only a hundred yards in front of me, was a Hellcat, its startled pilot trying to find my plane.

The fighters behind him were already turning at me. I didn't care how many there were. I wanted this fighter. The Hellcat jerked wildly to escape. Now! I squeezed, the tracers snapped out. My arms were too far gone. The Zero staggered; I couldn't keep my arms steady. The Hellcat rolled steeply, went into a climb and fled.

The loop had helped. The other fighters milled around in confusion. I climbed and ran for it again. The Grummans were right behind me.

The fools in those planes were firing from a distance of 500 yards. Waste your ammunition, waste it, waste it, I cried. But they were so fast! The tracers flashed by my wing and I rolled desperately.

Down below, Iwo suddenly appeared. I rocked my wings, hoping the gunners on the ground would see the red markings. It was a mistake. The maneuver slowed me down, and the Hellcats were all over me again.

Where was the flak? What's wrong with them down on the island? Open up, you fools, open up!

Iwo erupted in flame. Brilliant flashes swept across the island. They were firing all the guns, it seemed, spitting tracers into the air. Explosions rocked the Zero. Angry bursts of smoke appeared in the air among the Hellcats. They turned steeply and dove out of range.

I kept going at full speed. I was terrified. I kept looking behind me, fearing that they had come back, afraid that at any second the tracers wouldn't miss, that they'd stream into the cockpit, tearing away the metal, ripping into me.

I passed Iwo, banging my fist on the throttle, urging the plane to fly faster. Faster, faster! A giant cumulus, rearing high above the water, ahead of me. I didn't care about air currents. I wanted only to escape those fighters. At full speed I plunged into the billowy mass.

A tremendous fist seemed to seize the Zero and fling it wildly through the air. I saw nothing but vivid bursts of lightning, then blackness. I had no control. The Zero plunged and reared. It was upside down, falling, then standing on its wings and hurtling upward tail first.

Then I was through. The storm within the cloud spat the Zero out with a violent lurch. I was upside down. I regained control at less than 1,600 feet. Far to the south I caught a glimpse of fifteen Hellcats, going home to their carrier. It was hard to believe that it was all over and that I was still alive. I wanted desperately to get out of the air. I wanted solid ground beneath my feet . . .'

The battle of 24th June was the prelude to the end. With a loss of perhaps ten of their number, even

A rare picture: the moment before a stricken Zero breaks up

after being caught by surprise and bounced, the Hellcats shot half of the entire Japanese fighter force out of the sky.

And, as Sakai admitted with candor: 'The loss of forty planes and pilots in a single action staggered me. Equally disturbing was the sight of our inexperienced pilots falling in flames, one after the other, as the Hellcats blasted our outmoded Zeros from the sky. How much like Lae the battle had been! Except now the obsolescent planes were Zeros, and the inexperienced pilots were Japanese. The war had run full circle.'

In the next major battle the Hellcats shot down twenty of the remaining forty Zero fighters stationed at Iwo Jima. In a third battle another eleven were torn from the sky, leaving the Japanese with but nine weary fighters. Without even the outmoded Zero, Iwo Jima lay helpless to air attack.

But it had not always been that way.

Years before, it was the Zero that was master of the sky.

21

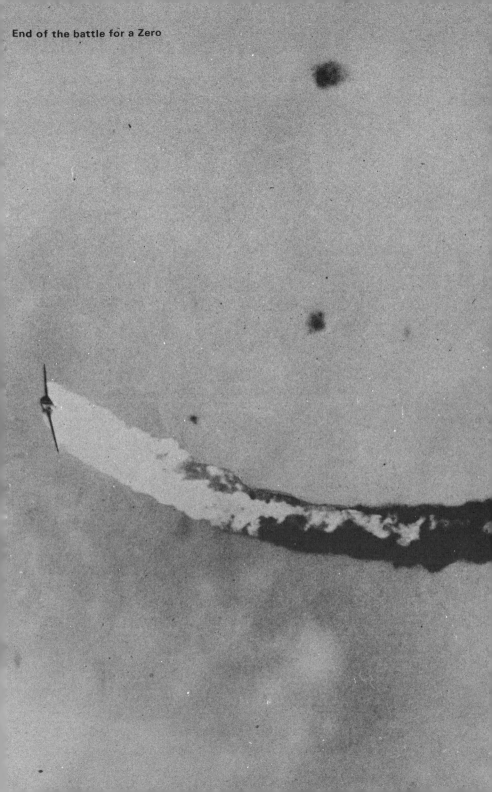

End of the battle for a Zero

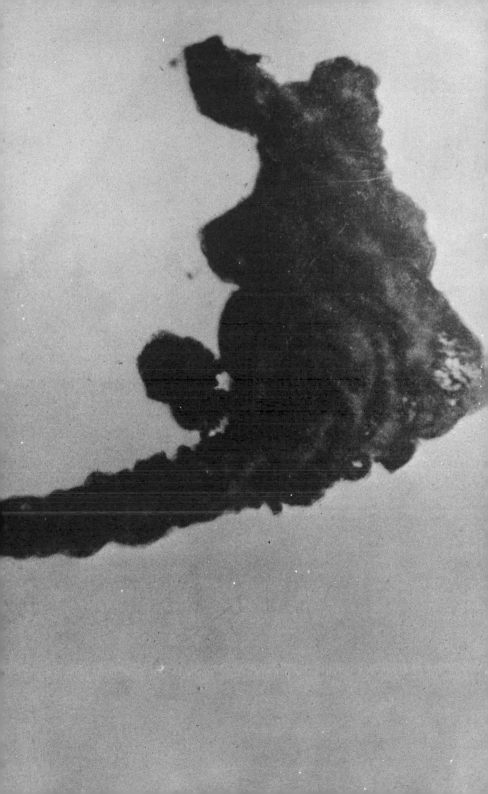

Changing the guard

The Second World War in the Pacific and Asia exploded behind a flying wedge of Japanese Zero fighters. On the first day of that war the United States lost two thirds of all its combat aircraft in the Pacific theater. The Japanese onslaught against Pearl Harbor effectively eliminated Hawaii as a source of immediate reinforcements for the Philippines. And on those beleagured islands, Japanese air attacks rapidly whittled down the remaining American air strength until it could no more than annoy a victory-flushed foe.

Of all the elements in the vast Japanese war machine that brought to pass that country's astonishing success, no single item was more important than the Zero fighter. Indeed, Japan's entire gamble rested on a single premise: that the Zero fighter could defeat, swiftly and surely, any fighters the Allies would put up against the sleek new machine produced by Mitsubishi. If the Zero could create an umbrella of air superiority wherever Japanese forces entered combat, then the outcome of the massive-front assault would never be in doubt.

The Zero fighter did everything expected of it, and more.

Japan controlled much of the vast China mainland at the time. She captured Guam and Wake. She overran the Netherlands East Indies. Singapore fell in humiliating defeat. Within a few months fearful anxiety gripped Australia as its cities were brought under air attack.

Everywhere the Zero swept the way clear for Japanese bombers, ships and troops.

Japanese aircraft swarmed almost uncontested against northern New Guinea, New Ireland, the Admiralties, New Britain and the Solomons. Enemy occupation of Kavieng, Rabaul and Bougainville not only threatened the precarious supply line from the United States to Australia, but became a potential springboard for the invasion of Australia itself.

Japan's victories merged into the shadow of the Zero fighter over the battlefronts.

The United States was openly astonished with the quality of Japanese equipment. It had committed the unforgivable sin of underestimating – severely – the caliber of Japanese designers, industry and men.

The United States entered the war convinced that nothing could stand up against American fighters. American pilots believed this to be so. That they nurtured this belief is astounding. Long before the air attack against Pearl Harbor the Japanese had flown the Zero in combat over the Chinese mainland. Intelligence reports were rushed to the United States.

No one believed them.

Aeronautical experts who studied the reports of performance of the new Japanese 'mystery fighter' snorted in disbelief. When they read the secret reports of speed, maneuverability, firepower and range they rejected as 'arrant nonsense' the claims that the Japanese had become a grim threat in the air.

Their conclusion was that such a fighter was literally an aerodynamic impossibility. That particular conclusion inevitably led to another, and thus the Americans' obsolete aircraft fell like flies before the agile, swift Zero.

The eminent British aviation historian, William Green, has noted that the Zero fighter was to the Japanese what the 'Spitfire was to the British nation. It symbolized Japan's conduct of the war, for as its fortune fared so fared the Japanese nation.'

Yet the Zero was even more important to the Japanese than the Spitfire to the British. The British fighter was used, primarily, to defend England against the onslaught of the German Luftwaffe. And although the Spitfire waged combat on almost every front it remained an aircraft limited severely by a short range, and despite its many offensive uses later in the war it made its niche in history primarily as the defense against the Messerschmitt Me-109 fighter in the Battle of Britain.

The position of the Zero in Japanese plans was analogous with that of the Me-109 in German plans. Both were intended for offensive thrusts against the enemy. Their entire purpose was to *attack*. Both were designed to destroy enemy fighters in the air and to protect their own offensive forces from strikes by enemy bombers. Never was their intended role primarily that of defense.

In retrospect, if we restrict ourselves to the early German and Japanese offensive campaigns, the Zero must be considered even more successful than its German contemporary. For the single greatest failing of the Me-109 during the massive air assault against the British Isles was its lack of range and endurance. Many historians are convinced that had the Germans built into their outstanding Me-109 additional range and endurance, the losses sustained by the defending Spitfires must inevitably have been much higher. History is quite explicit. Time and again the German escort pilots flying the Me-109 over England had to break off combat while the great air battles were still under way, leaving the bombers to the massed guns of Hurricanes and Spitfires.

The Zero, by comparison, had no such weakness. It could not only outperform any fighter against which it was matched, but could do so over extreme range – a range so great, in fact, that few air strategists believed the aircraft capable of such performance. Missions of 1,400 miles by the Zero fighter were commonplace at a time when the idea of Allied fighters flying from England to Berlin and back again was considered a fanciful dream.

Though vastly different in their origins, there are two complimentary evaluations of the Zero fighter which describe its importance. The first is that of William Green, and the second (of unquestioned value under any circumstances) is that of Jiro Horikoshi, the brilliant Japanese engineer who designed the Zero.

William Green has noted that: 'The Zero fighter marked the beginning of a new epoch in naval aviation: it was the first shipboard fighter capable of besting its land-based opponents. It created a myth – the myth of Japanese invincibility in the air, and one to which the Japanese themselves fell victim as a result of the almost total destruction of Allied air power in the early days of the Pacific war. In its day the Zero was the world's foremost carrier-based fighter, and its appearance over Pearl Harbor came as a complete surprise to the American forces. Its successive appearance over every major battle area in the opening days of the war seemed to indicate that Japan possessed unlimited supplies of this remarkable fighter, and its almost mystical powers of maneuver and ability to traverse vast stretches of water fostered the acceptance of the myth of its invincibility in Allied minds.'

Now let us see how the aircraft, and its reception by the Allied forces, was regarded by the man who designed the fighter, the brilliant Jiro Horikoshi, architect of a series of Japan's most outstanding fighters. This is Horikoshi's account:

'Ever since the attack which the Nagumo Force launched against Pearl Harbor in December of 1941, one of the "unsolved mysteries" of aviation has been the origin of certain Japanese military aircraft. During the Pacific War we in Japan received reports primarily concerning the Zero fighter. We understood, and postwar revelations confirmed this, that the appearance of this aircraft took the United States and Allies completely by surprise.

Since that time I have heard descriptions of the A6M Zeke or Zero fighter which, at one extreme, was called the "wonder fighter", and at the other extreme was labelled "a poor copy of older American fighters". Neither of these two exaggerations is, of course, correct. The Zero was not a "wonder" aircraft, but rather the product of intensive studies, which, for several years after its introduction to combat in 1940, gave it a definite superiority over opposing enemy machines. To remark that the Zero was a copy is only to reveal ignorance of aeronautical design.

The Zero was received with great surprise when it made its first appearance against the Americans and, later, the British. This in itself is astonishing, since this airplane flew in action in China some eighteen months before the attack on Pearl Harbor. We found it difficult to believe that the Zero, which had flown thousands of sorties over the Chinese mainland, should have remained such a secret to our opponents in the Pacific War.

From early 1940, when the Zero entered service, until late 1942, when the United States first introduced to the Pacific theater the Lightning and Corsair fighters, the Zero enjoyed undisputed mastery over nearly every enemy aircraft it encountered. Our failure to produce in quantity the successors to the Zero, especially the high-performance Reppu [Allied code name Sam] (Mitsubishi A7M), lost us the decisive advantage which we had enjoyed during the early part of the war.

The Zero was the product of a given set of circumstances. The design answered specifically the unique requirements of Japanese pilots, who stressed the factor of unexcelled maneuverability. Much has been said of the Zero fighter's lack of pilot protection devices, such as armor plate and self-sealing fuel tanks. These items were omitted from the Zero at the insistence of our pilots. To them, fighting in the air meant only one thing: attack. They would not tolerate the encumbering weight of accessories designed solely for protective purposes. They felt that the gain in performance resulting from minimum weight more than compensated for a lack of safety features which, to them, represented unnecessary luxury.

For several years this philosophy proved its validity in the extraordinary ratio of enemy aircraft destroyed as against the number of Zeros lost in combat. As the war progressed, however, and as the Allies introduced new fighters possessing greater firepower and speed, the requirements of our pilots also began to change. Despite the modifications to the Zero, which included those pilot protection features originally scorned, the airplane essentially was limited in performance by an engine which failed to keep pace with Allied horsepower ratings, and by disastrous industrial problems created by enemy bombing, earthquakes, and a worsening materials problem.

It is true that for many years the Japanese aeronautical industry leaned heavily upon foreign design and craftsmanship. This situation, necessitated by Japan's belated acceptance of the Industrial Revolution, we endeavored to correct as rapidly as possible. By 1936, when we adopted the (Mitsubishi A5M 'Claude') Type 96 series of aircraft, we were able to abandon the policy of following foreign designs and of relying upon foreign manufacturing techniques. While certain important segments of our industry still looked to the rest of the world, in the fields of airframe and enginé design, flying skill and air tactics we enjoyed independence.

We believe that by 1936 the performance of original Japanese-designed small and medium-sized aircraft and air-cooled engines had reached the level of the world's best. By that time our pilots were flying the A5M 'Claude' carrier fighter and the G3M 'Nell' attack bomber, both completed in 1935. However, this transition to independent design could not be accomplished overnight. We admitted that certain categories of airframe and engine structure, accessories, aircraft armament, and the majority of our instruments could not hope to overtake the exceptional progress of certain foreign designers. The fact that all Japanese aircraft were equipped with items manufactured under foreign license, or which were copied from foreign design, is undeniable. But the independence achieved in airframe and engine design, in new peaks of flying skill and aerial tactics, is equally unmistakable.

By 1936–37 the Japanese aeronautical industry, especially that part which supported our naval aviation, clearly stood on its own legs. Indeed, so rapidly did this military [i.e. naval] branch progress that in many respects we forged ahead of comparable foreign achievements. We developed certain types of aircraft to meet specific combat requirements and, in so doing, achieved in these categories a marked superiority over comparable foreign products.

In aerial tactics our naval aviation exhibited special and unparalleled skill. For the first time in the history of air warfare we employed long-range fighters to achieve command of the air over the enemy's territory. This was accomplished in 1937 during the Sino-Japanese Incident, long before such procedures were regarded as necessary by the remainder of the world.

Indeed, in China the Zero flew non-stop sorties of 1,400 miles, a perfor-

The thirty-three year old Jiro Horikoshi in 1936, at this time – as he says – 'between Claude and Zero'

mance considered impossible by other nations.'

As Horikoshi makes clear, the Zero fighter did not spring into existence overnight. For years prior to his designing the Mitsubishi Type 00 fighter, Horikoshi was hard at work on a series of fighter and other designs.

Although Horikoshi was largely an unknown in world aeronautical circles in comparison with the designers of such world-famous aircraft as the Spitfire, Hurricane and Me-109, within the hierarchy of Japan he had already achieved extraordinary recognition and respect for his brilliant design and engineering work. Horikoshi designed the first monoplane fighter for the Japanese navy, the Type 96 (A5M Claude), the aircraft that shattered enemy opposition on the Chinese mainland and which catapulted the Japanese navy into a position of swiftly growing international power. This is where the story of the Zero fighter starts – 1934, and the creation of the Type 96 fighter.

The new fighters

An obscure figure in aviation – outside Japan, that is – was responsible for the sudden acceleration of Japanese fighter designs to equal any in the world. Lieutenant-Commander Hideo Sawai, a staff member of the Japanese Naval Bureau of Aeronautics, was one of many top Japanese aviation leaders who in 1934 recognised the need for drastic changes in Japanese fighter design philosophy. The 7-*Shi* (the *Shi* designation was numbered from the beginning of the Emperor Hirohito's reign in 1926, and thus the 7-*Shi* series was called for in the seventh year of Hirohito's reign, i.e. 1932) series of fighters for the Imperial Japanese Navy were barely short of engineering disasters, and both Mitsubishi and Nakajima, which had built the experimental carrier fighters, were still smarting from the jibes and criticisms hurled at them by everyone from pilots to admirals. The criticisms were less than pleasant. Japan counted upon a new generation of carrier-based fighter aircraft to extend the sphere of Japanese influence throughout Asia. Unlike other world powers the Japan-

ese fully appreciated the effect of airpower and were pressing vigorously to translate doctrine into hardware. Faced with aircraft of poor performance in the 7-*Shi* series, the navy showed an unexpected willingness to listen to Commander Sawai. He insisted that the time given to the manufacturers for designing and producing the 7-*Shi* fighters was inadequate. The requirements for carrier equipment, he added, were excessive. But what proved most unforgivable, Sawai argued, was the policy of government interference with the men and the companies responsible for producing the new combat aircraft. The design teams, he insisted, must be left to their own devices. The navy, to everyone's great surprise, reversed its former policies and went ahead with Sawai's recommendations.

'It should be stated for the record,' asserts Jiro Horikoshi, 'that the Mitsubishi 9-*Shi* fighter was almost

A biplane, soon to be superceded by the new Japanese monoplanes, passes over Japanese troops in China

assured of success when the original specifications for the series were issued by the Japanese Naval Bureau of Aeronautics. The normally expected ability to land on aircraft carrier decks, with the accompanying incorporation of carrier fighting equipment into the initial prototype, was conspicuously absent from the original specifications. The design requirements forwarded by the Navy for the 9-*Shi* single-seat fighter were, therefore, of a most general nature, and allowed myself and my staff wide latitude in our development program. ... I was fortunate in that my original staff, who had worked with me on the 7-*Shi* fighter, was still almost intact. Since each man, and the group as a whole, had benefited from the knowledge and experience of working on the 7-*Shi* fighter, I was able to incorporate into my new design several novel ideas which represented a marked change over former practice. ... The paramount factors involved in improving the performance of a fighter included the reduction of the aircraft's air resistance and its total weight. I stressed these two factors in designing the new fighter. ... The basic configuration was to be that of an internally braced low-wing monoplane . . . with streamlining carried down to the smallest detail. Every effort would be made to reduce resistance from skin friction to a minimum.'

On 4th February 1935, at Kaganigahara Airfield, about fifteen miles north of Nagoya, Test Pilot Kajima took the new 9-*Shi* fighter, which was to be designated the A5M, into the air for its first tests. Before the day ended jubilation among the Mitsubishi staff knew no bounds. The lithe A5M had flown at nearly 280 mph in level flight – far exceeding the requirement of 218 mph. The aircraft handled beautifully, reported Kajima, and its stability and controllability were outstanding. In the ensuing weeks the A5M bested its rival in the 1934 competition, the fighter built by Nakajima. Mitsubishi had come through with a brilliant design. Jiro Horikoshi and his design team wasted little time in self-congratulation. They had a severe program ahead of them in testing new prototypes, and

fitting one of the A5M fighters with carrier gear.

Two problems quickly showed. When the A5M flew at a high angle of attack (the angle between the chord of the wing and the horizontal) it would sometimes develop a severe pitching movement, and it was necessary to correct a situation that could prove disastrous in combat. The second problem came during landing. The A5M had a tendency to balloon, or to float down the runway instead of sinking steadily as it neared the ground.

Modifications to the wing eliminated the pitching tendencies, and the introduction of wing flaps to increase drag during landing eliminated the floating characteristics.

The test program showed the A5M to have a maximum speed of 279 mph in level flight at 10,500 feet – a tremendous advance in performance. Equally important, the A5M could climb from a standing start to a height of 16,400 feet in 5 minutes 54 seconds.

By comparison, the Gloster Gladiator of 1934, considered one of the world's leading fighters by European experts, had a maximum speed of 253 mph at 14,500 feet, and a rate of climb of 4.8 minutes to 15,000 feet.

The success of the new A5M fighter in its flight tests was such that the Japanese navy immediately cancelled its orders for fighter aircraft of foreign manufacture that had been scheduled to be introduced into Japanese service. The only orders which the Japanese retained were for fighter aircraft to be tested against the A5M – two French Dewoitine D-510 aircraft. Once again the Japanese were confirmed in their solid trust in Mitsubishi's new whirlwind – the swift and agile A5M bested the D-510 in every mock battle flown.

The production orders were rushed through. Nearly 1,000 were eventually produced by Mitsubishi, the Sasebo Navy Air Depot and the Kyushu Aircraft Company.

The acid test of any fighter is combat. Despite the tremendous success in test and engineering flights of the new A5M fighter, it could not be considered fully proved until its pilots flew it in battle against enemy op-

Above: Prototype Claude 1 with cranked wings. It went into a power dive and crashed. *Below:* Prototype Claude 2 which went into a flat spin during a test flight and crashed. Horikoshi abandoned both prototypes due to their poor performances

position. The explosive spread of war in China in 1937 brought the A5M into combat sooner than anyone had expected.

The demand for the A5M fighters also was unexpected. The Japanese were still experimenting with combat tactics for dive and level bombers, and these experiments resulted in grisly losses when the unescorted bombers were attacked by swarms of fighters defending Chinese targets. The defending fighters were flown by Chinese, Americans, Frenchmen, some Italians, a few Germans, and even Russians. The nationality of the pilots mattered little to the Japanese, of course, nor were they concerned by the many different type of fighters used. What alarmed them was that Japanese bombers were being cut to ribbons.

Referring to the opening period of the Sino-Japanese Incident, General Masatake Okumiya (former Commander, Imperial Japanese Navy) noted: 'Despite the quality of our planes and the caliber of our pilots, the Navy's Air Force suffered heavy losses in the early days of the incident. There was much to be learned in the art of long-distance attack which could be acquired in peacetime, but the price which the Chinese exacted for those lessons was severe. We learned – almost at once, and with devastating thoroughness – that bombers are no match for enemy fighter planes. . . . The planes of the aircraft carrier *Kaga* suffered disastrously. The twelve Type 89 carrier-based attack bombers, led by Group-Commander Iawai, left the *Kaga* on 17th August for a raid against Hangchou. Bad weather prevented a rendezvous with an expected fighter escort and near their target the bombers were attacked by a group of Chinese fighter planes. Eleven bombers . . . were shot down. Lieutenant (J G) Tanaka managed to bring his bullet-riddled and crippled bomber safely back to the carrier; otherwise, the fate of the attacking group would never have

been known. . . . We discovered that when our fighter planes provided escort to, over, and from the target such incidents did not occur. Comparing the shattered unescorted bomber groups with the relatively unharmed formations which were protected by fighters, the Navy reacted quickly. The *Kaga* was ordered to return immediately to Sasebo and to receive a full complement of the new Type 96 carrier-based fighters (Claudes).

The fighter pilots defending China's cities and military targets had not the slightest inkling that a carrier loaded with a new Japanese fighter was on its way to the combat theater. Until now the Japanese fighters encountered in the air were slow biplanes of spectacular maneuverability. For the greatest part surprise and pilot skill more than outstanding aircraft performance determined the outcome of battle. All that was to change.

The A5M Claude was a sleek monoplane. Its fixed undercarriage was designed cleanly for minimum drag. The aircraft proved unusually fast, but opposing pilots were surprised to note that the A5M had an open cockpit, whereas European designs were beginning to introduce enclosed cockpits. The fact of the matter was that the Japanese pilots, who had flown the A5M with the closed canopies, protested bitterly that it reduced their visibility. Mitsubishi hurriedly removed the canopies and reverted to open cockpits.

On 18th September 1937 the new Mitsubishi fighters went into action for the first time, flying as escorts with the Second Combined Air Flotilla in a strike against Nanking. The defending pilots were eager to hit at the Japanese again. They had shattered Japanese formations time and again and they were thirsty for fresh blood.

The Japanese were quite ready to oblige. They sent in the new Mitsubishi fighters, and a factor on which the Japanese counted heavily was superb leadership. Commanding the fighter forces were Lieutenant-Commanders Okamura and Genda, and Lieutenants Nomura and Nango, famous within the navy for their

Flight Petty Officer Kashimura, who became a national hero, autographed this picture of his Claude flying over Japanese warships during the Sino-Japanese incident in 1936

Mitsubishi 3GM Nells. These bombers were escorted in raids on China by carrier borne A5M Claudes and the early Zeros

outstanding skill.

The Chinese fighters included the Boeing P-26, Curtiss Hawk II and Hawk III, and Italian Fiats. They rushed eagerly against the incoming bomber formations and their new escorts.

It did not take long for the new facts of war to become clear. The Japanese had come to kill and they were going at their task with a terrible efficiency. The Mitsubishi pilots flew a lithe killer that was faster in level flight, outclimbed any of the Chinese collection of fighters, and whirled through maneuvers that not even the slower biplane fighters flown by the Chinese could follow.

In the weeks ensuing the air battles grew in size and intensity, and the Japanese repeated consistently the stunning success gained with the new Mitsubishi fighter. The Japanese navy concentrated its raid with formations of dive bombers escorted by the A5Ms. The Chinese made desperate attempts to gather new fighters to replace the heavy losses they were suffering. In addition to the types mentioned they threw into battle British Gloster Gladiators as well as Russian biplane and monoplane fighters. The Japanese swarmed into the new arrivals with increasing skill. In two months the Claudes had swept the sky clear of opposition. The final combat of the period was on 2nd December 1937 when a force of A5M fighters, led by Lieutenant Nango, decimated a Russian force by shooting down ten intercepting Polikarpov I-16 fighters.

Only two Russian fighters escaped destruction. The Japanese left the

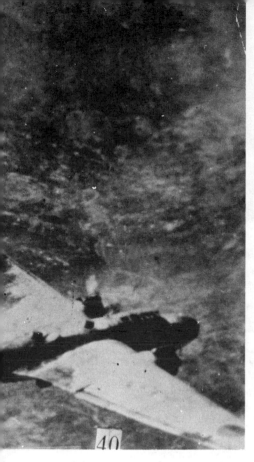

40

long-standing controversy in Japan, destroying once and for all the validity of the arguments of those who insisted upon retaining biplane-type fighters. Even with due consideration for its exceptional maneuverability, the short range and slow speed of the Type 95 carrier-based fighter doomed it to extinction. It required the final test of combat to determine which of these two fighter types would be the most effective in war.

There were other lessons which the Japanese heeded. The air war, as well as the ground war in China, promised to be long, costly and spread out over great distances. If the Japanese pursued their proven doctrine of always pressing home the attack, of striking at the enemy far beyond the front lines, they would soon outrun the range of their covering fighters.

The Mitsubishi Type 96 was essentially a fighter of limited range. Up to this point it met almost every combat requirement. That situation, the Japanese knew, would not remain unchanged. They would be sending bombers deep into enemy territory, and without fighter escort. To the Japanese leaders the results were clearly predictable: unescorted bombers were dead meat for defending fighters.

The Japanese started a new fighter program – the 12-*Shi*. It would become known as the Zero, but it would not be available for some time.

In the interim the worst fears of the Japanese were realised. Japanese bombers ranged deep into Chinese territory. 'The limited range of the A5M fighters,' noted Okumiya, 'prevented them from escorting the bombers to their objectives, where waiting Chinese fighters pounced upon the raiders. We suffered heavy losses . . . During some raids the percentage of lost or damaged bombers rose beyond the "prohibitive" figure of ten per cent. The Chinese fighters inflicted at least half the damage sustained by our bombers, while anti-aircraft fire was responsible for the remainder. We could alleviate this unsatisfactory situation only by securing command of the air over the targets.'

The answer was to be the Zero fighter, which was already well into

battle area without a single loss.

The first phase of the long air war to come in Chinese skies was over, and the Japanese unquestionably were the overwhelming victors.

There would be many more air battles involving the Mitsubishi A5M fighters, but the issue of quality would never be in doubt. General Masatake Okumiya, reviewing the lessons of that period in the air war, noted that for the Japanese navy, many lessons were gained in the way of new tactics and operations from the campaign, especially (1) that air groups and combat aircraft trained at sea for sea duty can serve successfully without special training in any air campaign over land, and (2) that the key to success in any land or sea operation depends upon command of the air.

The outstanding combat successes of the Type 96 (A5M) fighters ended a

Mitsubishi A5M Claude, presumably in a training unit as the *Hinomarus* (Rising Sun emblems) are surrounded by a white border, indicating that the aircraft was photographed after 3rd July 1943, after the A5M had been phased out of active service

accelerated development.

As Okumiya has emphasised, the success of the A5M fighter in Chinese skies vanquished more than one opponent. Jiro Horikoshi touched on this when, referring to the opening phases of development of the Zero, he remarked that the success of the A5M enabled the Navy to discard many of its antiquated design concepts, and to accept the aerodynamic innovations requisite for high performance.

On 19th May 1937 (the twelfth year of *Showa*) the navy submitted to Mitsubishi and Nakajima a draft of the design specifications for the 12-*Shi* carrier fighter, which was eventually to replace the A5M.

Changes came faster than expected. There was war in Asia and the Japanese were stiffening their military backbone wherever they ran into opposition from other countries contesting Japanese concepts of expansion. The navy felt the new fighter might be needed much sooner than had been anticipated and, at the same time, with an eye to fighter development and performance from European countries, modified its own design specifications by demanding still higher performance.

The general specifications for the 12-*Shi* fighter were:

1. Purpose: Interceptor fighter capable of destroying enemy attack bombers; and escort fighter with combat performance superior to that of enemy interceptors.

2. Speed: Maximum level speed to exceed 310.5 mph at 13,125 feet (4,000 metres).

3. Climb: Climb to 9,840 feet within 3 minutes 30 seconds.

4. Duration: Normal flight duration 1.2 to 1.5 hours, with normal rated power at 9,840 feet. Overload duration (auxiliary tanks) 1.5 to 2.0 hours at 9,840 feet with normal rated power; or 6 to 8 hours at cruising speed.

5. Takeoff: Less than 229.7 feet with headwind of 30 mph.

6. Landing Speed: Less than 66.7 mph.

7. Gliding (power off) Descent: 690 to 787 feet per minute.

8. Maneuverability: At least equal to that of the A5M.

9. Armament: Two 20-mm cannon and two 7.7-mm machine guns.

10. Bombs: Two 66-lb bombs (Overload). Two 132-lb bombs (Overload).
11. Radio: Type 96-Ku-1 airborne radio. Kiuisi Type Ku-3 homing equipment (Goniometer).
12. Other Equipment: Oxygen system. Fire extinguisher. Lighting equipment. Instruments.

The 12-*Shi* fighter specifications demanded a major step beyond what the Horikoshi team had achieved with the A5M. The Japanese engineers were taken aback by the performance demands as laid down by the navy, since it demanded speed, rate of climb, and armament which were at least equal to the highest levels in Japan and, in fact, in the world. In addition, the Mitsubishi team was required to deliver exceptional maneuverability and range.

'The navy's specifications,' noted Jiro Horikoshi, 'exceeded the aeronautical engineering standards hitherto accepted in Japan. Obviously it would be impossible, through conventional methods, to fulfill the requirements for the new aircraft, since the demand for speed, rate of climb, turning radius, range, pilot vision, takeoff and landing performance *each* equalled or bettered the outstanding individual features of the world's best fighters.

'The range of the 12-*Shi* project warranted the use of a radio homing equipment, in itself a revolutionary step for a fighter. Few fighters in the late 1930s carried wing-mounted 20-mm cannon, and these were experimental, not operational, installations; designers regarded the wing-mounted cannon with disfavor because of their poor accuracy in combat. . . . One can judge the validity of any aircraft specification only by attempting to analyse the performance of the aircraft several years after the initiation of the design program and by comparing it with the anticipated level of foreign design. I assumed that, on the basis of Japan's industrial potential in 1937, three years would pass before the 12-*Shi* fighter became operational. I allowed one year for design work, six months for prototype construction, another year for flight testing and modifications, and an additional six months for limited initial production. This three-year figure allowed possible overlapping of each specific phase of work, as well as possible engineering changes dictated by the navy.'

On 17th January 1938 engineers and naval officers convened in a naval-civilian joint investigation conference in Yokosuka. There the group listened to. Lieutenant-Commander Genda, only five days returned from combat in China; Genda detailed the lessons learned in air fighting, and how these should affect any new fighter design. Genda's words sparked a heated, openly controversial discussion. The Navy reiterated its need for the new 12-*Shi* fighter, stressing that the high performance demands must be met. Many engineers, openly dismayed, stated flatly that the requirements were impossible. The navy refused to budge.

The delegation from Nakajima made their position clear. The new fighter, they said, could not be built, and the company was withdrawing from the competition.

That left the Mitsubishi team under Jiro Horikoshi. Assisting him in his work were Yoshitoshi Sone and Teruo Tojo for mathematical calculations; Sone and Yoshio Yoshikawa for structural work; Denichiro Inouye and Shotaro Tanaka for research into powerplant installation; Yoshimi Hatakenaka for armament and auxiliary equipment; and Sadahiko Kato and Takeyoshi Moror for landing gear and related equipment.

The new fighter was into its first pangs of birth.

To power the new fighter, the Horikoshi team selected, as a result of naval power loading requirements, the Mitsubishi MK2 *Zuisei* 13 engine, a fourteen-cylinder twin-row radial which produced a maximum of 875 horsepower (the engine was later to be designated Ha.31/13). The engine was particularly suited to the 12-*Shi* design because of its light weight and small diameter. After several conflicting decisions the navy directed Mitsubishi to. mount a two-bladed Sumitomo Hamilton constant-speed propeller on the prototype fighter then under construction. The constant-speed propeller enabled the 12-*Shi* prototype to utilize fully the engine's available horsepower.

With power limited to a specific engine the key to the fighter's performance would lie in the direction of minimum weight and minimum drag. 'Weight saving,' Horikoshi has said, 'became the most important single goal in the design program. By constructing the wing as a single piece, we eliminated the usual bulky and heavy fittings between the inner and outer wing sections, employing only small fittings for fuselage-wing joints. We gained in the battle of weight through use of a new material, Sumitomo's Extra-Super Duralumin, "ESD", which went into the main spar caps. Semi-permanent connections between the wing and fuselage allowed us to detach the after half of the fuselage from the forward part by disengaging several dozen connecting bolts. . . . By eliminating the usual complicated large fittings of alloy steels we not only reduced the total weight, but minimized the number of forging and machining operations on the production lines. . . . I devoted much care to reducing air drag, and to refining stability and controllability. To achieve a more stable "firing platform" for the 20 mm cannon, I extended to slightly longer than normal the fuselage length. A raised bubble canopy provided excellent pilot visibility. . . .

Excellent maneuverability demanded a low wing loading, and for the prototype we aimed at a figure of 21.5 pounds per square foot. Although the disadvantages of reduced level and dive speeds accompanied this, it was necessary to incur these unsatisfactory characteristics to meet the navy's demands for a small turning radius and for low-landing and takeoff speeds. Eventually, the fighter's outstanding agility in combat proved its greatest asset; on the other hand, its inability to dive at a high rate of speed hampered it greatly when it engaged the faster and heavier American fighter planes . . . In later months our attention to even the most minute aerodynamic details time and again proved their worth. In a performance contest with the army's Oscar (Nakajima Ki-44 *Hayabusa*) fighter, equipped with the same engine and a constant-speed propeller, the Zero proved superior in maximum speed, diving, zooming, and general dogfighting characteristics. The Zero weighed more than the Oscar and carried a greater useful load.'

Strange to relate, the 12-*Shi* fighter ran into a storm of controversy even as the prototype neared completion. The argument raged over the relative merits demanded in Japan's future fighter aircraft for naval use.

Lieutenant-Commander Minouru Genda, the highly respected combat leader with extensive experience in Chinese air combat, opted for maneuverability as the primary requisite for the 12-*Shi* design. Genda was more than a brilliant military leader, he was also an outstanding, even a brilliant aerobatic pilot and had been the leader of the famed 'Genda Circus', composed of Japan's four best aerobatic pilots. The Japanese naval command paid close attention to Genda's conclusions and what he offered as the best requirements for a new fighter.

During a crucial meetings, which could well affect the final outcome of the 12-*Shi* program, Genda left no doubts as to his feelings. 'In a fighter,' he said, 'particularly a carrier-based fighter, I believe the single most important characteristic is the ability of the airplane to engage successfully in close-in fighting – dogfighting, as you will. Maneuverability is unmistakably the fighter's most valuable performance requirement, and we should accept a corresponding loss in speed and range in order to secure this necessary agility.'

Directly opposed to the views of Genda was Lieutenant-Commander Takeo Shibata, at the time the chief test pilot of the Naval Aircraft Establishment. Shibata was also a crack combat pilot, and as one of Japan's leading test pilots, his words carried the same authority as those of Genda.

'Japanese fighters,' insisted Shibata, 'are undisputedly superior in dogfighting performance to the best aircraft of foreign nations. This excellent maneuverability, however, has not allowed our fighter aircraft to participate in many battles in which they have been desperately needed. More than maneuverability is required. We made a serious error in the air war over China; we misjudged, sometimes disastrously, the ability of the Type 96 land-based attack bomber to raid enemy positions with relative impunity. Because these planes sustained losses, far heavier than we anticipated, it is clear that the bombers must be escorted by fighters.

For this purpose we need a single-seat fighter with both long range and high speed. I do not believe that the answer lies in large, heavy, twin-engined fighter escorts, as some people have proposed. These will never suffice. The escort fighter should be as fast as possible, for even the slightest superior margin in speed will allow our planes to pursue and destroy escaping enemy planes. I believe that inadequate maneuverability in a fighter can be more than compensated for by the superior skill of its pilot. I am firmly convinced that I myself could train our navy fighter pilots to maintain a clear super·ority over enemy fighters, even with aircraft of inferior turning radius. But I remind you that the maximum speed of an airplane is strictly limited by its power and the design of the airplane, and that even the best pilot cannot through his own skill make an airplane fly faster than its designed maximum performance. Conversely, in dogfights, outstanding pilot skill can endow our men with a clear superiority, easily compensating for lack of maneuverability.

As the chief test pilot for the Naval Aircraft Establishment I insist that speed and range be given priority over dogfighting performance.'

The conference group was split wide open by the opposing views of Genda and Shibata. What further complicated the discussion was that both men were close friends, sincere in their beliefs, and with only the best interests of Japan in mind. There were no personal issues involved. Another problem that confounded the conference was that there did not exist a single officer of higher rank than Genda or Shibata with the experience necessary to render a decision that would be not only the right one, but technically accurate in terms of the issues that were involved.

For hours the military and naval conferees struggled at an impasse and they were all aware, as Masatake Okumiya put it, that obviously someone must make a decision, for the work on the A6M – 12-*Shi* fighter could not be delayed until the issue was resolved to the satisfaction of all. '. . . At the time of the conference, I participated in the discussions as both the Division Officer of the dive-bomber forces of the Yokosuka Air Corps and as a member of the Battle Lessons Committee. The conference adjourned, still seeking a clear-cut policy decision on fighter aircraft, and the Mitsubishi engineering team returned to their work more determined than ever to produce a fighter which would satisfy all parties concerned.'

The A6M fighter hung perilously close to extinction in the weeks that followed. The results of intensive studies, interrogation of pilots, evaluation of combat reports, and an extrapolation of future combat needs was brought to Mitsubishi in the form of a crushing blow.

The majority of the pilots involved – and their stand was being supported by naval high command – opted for maneuverability as the prime requisite in a new fighter. What disturbed the Horikoshi design team so profoundly was that maneuverability was to be achieved at almost any cost. The new primary performance standards called for a flight endurance of only one hour and thirty minutes of combat at full throttle, then return to base. This negated almost completely Horikoshi's intention to build a fighter that could fly almost anywhere Japanese forces would be involved in combat. Even more startling was the overwhelming decision to abandon the 20mm cannon Horikoshi had designed into the 12-*Shi* fighter, the prototype of which was even then nearing completion. The Japanese pilots, accustomed to fighting at close range, insisted that machine-gun fire was more than effective for their dogfighting needs.

'These opinions,' explained Okumiya, 'supported by the Yokosuka Experimental Air Corps, differed greatly from the navy's prevailing attitude during that time when the first A6M (12-*Shi*) was being conceived. The reports could be taken only as expressing the operational

Above: **The first large scale production variant of the Zero, the A6M2.**
Below: **The A6M5 model of the Zero, the most numerous variant**

corps' dissatisfaction with the embryonic 12-*Shi* fighter, the main assets of which were long range and 20mm cannon. The ranking officers of the Aircraft Establishment and. the Bureau of Aeronautics thus found it necessary to review critically the entire 12-*Shi* program, and the Bureau requested Jiro Horikoshi to submit as quickly as possible the basic design and performance estimates of the "lightweight carrier-based fighter" which meets the demands of the 12th Air Corps.'

Horikoshi concealed his irritation with these demands. But presented as they were in all good faith by the Bureau, and representing the conclusive opinion of the majority of fighter pilots and experienced air leaders, he complied at once – convinced that he and his design team were still on the right track, and that their original 12-*Shi* design represented the best possible fighter aircraft in the world.

Horikoshi complied with the demands placed on him, but once he completed his studies of the new fighter aircraft, and they agreed with his original estimates, his back stiffened. Now he had the hard facts with which to support beyond all question his convictions. Horikoshi brought the design estimates of the new fighter to the navy and in incisive terms showed, beyond all question, that the original 12-*Shi* design, on which he and his team had labored for some time, remained superior to the fighter demanded by the Bureau.

Specifically, Horikoshi stated flatly, according to Okumiya, 'that the aircraft as requested by the 12th Air Corps would fail to match the overall efficiency of the aircraft already under construction. The navy's attitude wavered before an adamant Horikoshi. Finally, subjected also to the pressure of the entire Mitsubishi aircraft design staff who were in full accord with their chief designer, the navy relented and once again lent full support to the 12-*Shi* project.'

The aircraft that was destined to become one of the world's greatest fighters had survived its first blow – even while it was still taking form on the floor of the Mitsubishi factory.

On 16th March 1939 the 'Prototype No 1' of the 12-*Shi* fighter project stood completed in the Mitsubishi factory at Nagoya. Now began the long series of tests designed to prove the aircraft's actual performance. First in the schedule for 18th March were the initial engine tests. 'The engineers were jubilant,' states the official report. 'The engine and its auxiliary components, all instruments, valves, switches, propeller, and other equipment functioned perfectly.'

The day following, 19th March, Horikoshi ordered the 12-*Shi* prototype transferred from the Nagoya factory to the flight test field of Kagamigahara airfield twenty-five miles distant. The Nagoya factory, thanks to very poor planning on the part of both Mitsubishi and the navy, lacked even a single runway for flight operations!

'The transfer operation,' states Okumiya, 'was ridiculous.' And indeed it was, as the sleek new fighter aircraft was attached by rope to a slow and cumbersome ox-drawn cart. The Mitsubishi design team ground their teeth in frustration as their gleaming aircraft moved at a creaking and groaning pace to the military flight strip.

Extensive ground testing at Kagamigahara revealed minor equipment problems which were corrected quickly. Horikoshi announced the fighter was ready for the acid test of flight.

Jiro Horikoshi personally selected the test pilot for this flight, the most critical juncture in Horikoshi's career. Katsuzo Shima was described by Horikoshi as an 'outstanding and skilled flier'. The Mitsubishi test pilot was a retired petty officer third class, who after his retirement flew as a test pilot for the Flight Testing Division, Naval Aircraft Establishment. In 1938, Mitsubishi Heavy Industries Ltd employed him as a test pilot, and he later became Senior Test Pilot.

As specified in the test schedules the 12-*Shi* fighter prototype was to make its initial flight with only half its normal fuel and oil capacity. To prevent any unexpected problems Horikoshi ordered the landing gear locked in the down position. At take-

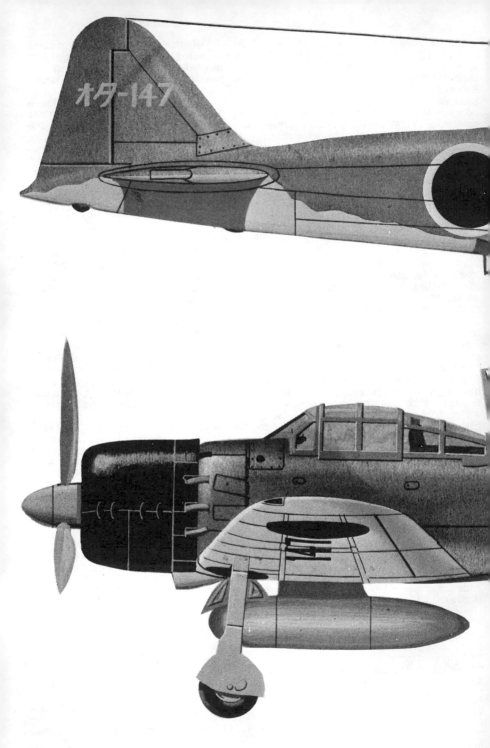

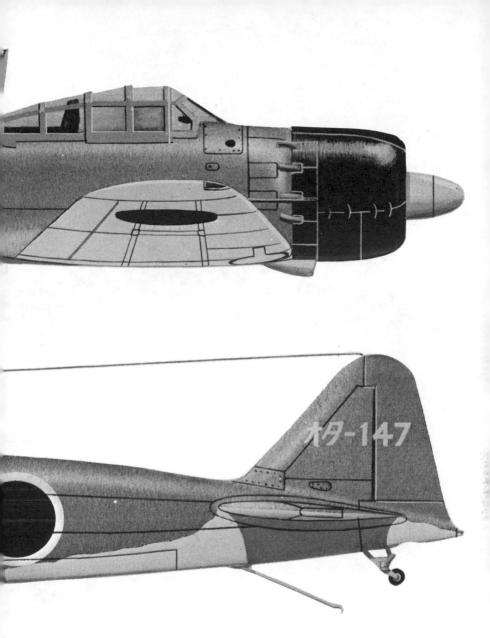

Mitsubishi A6M5: note the clean and economical cowling of the radial engine and the exhaust ejector stubs, fitted for the first time on the Zero in its A6M5 version. Also noteworthy are the full all-round vision cockpit canopy, the overall clean design and the ability to carry a long-range fuel tank under the fuselage, a feature designed into the aircraft from the earliest design stage, before the war. The white ring round the fuselage *hinomaru* (the Japanese red disc national marking) indicates that this aircraft was in action in July 1943 at the earliest. The general cleanliness of the fighter is emphasised in this view of it with its landing gear retracted

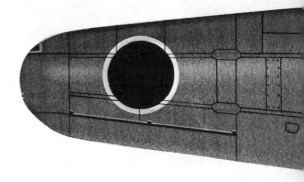

Mitsubishi A6M5 (top view): noteworthy in this view is the all-round vision cockpit canopy, which gave the pilot a good view over the nose to the front and also slightly downwards. Also noteworthy is the exceptionally clean installation of the basically bulky radial power plant, which does not in the least mar the slim and well tapered lines of the fuselage

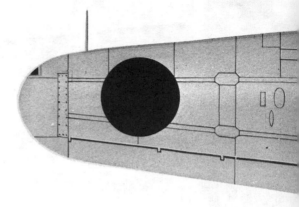

Mitsubishi A6M5 (underneath view): the view from this angle clearly indicates
some of the reasons for the Zero's outstanding maneuvrability – the short
fuselage and the generous area of wing, complete with long-span ailerons
and clean lines. The rear fuselage could have been made shorter by a small amount,
but the designer decided to keep it at this length to improve the aerodynamic
qualities of the fighter as a gun platform

off the 12-*Shi* weighed 4,380 pounds.

Masatake Okumiya recorded the events of the day thus:

'As the time for the first flight approached, all flying activity over and in the vicinity of the vast airfield was halted. The ground crew rolled the aircraft from its hangar and engineer Kumataro Takenaka climbed into the cockpit. He started the engine; the airscrew blades turned slowly, then faster and faster as the engine's roar boomed across the field. Takenaka gradually opened the throttle, then alternately increased and decreased the engine's speed. He studied carefully the performance of the engine, the instruments, the engine controls, and the primary control system. Everything checked out perfectly.

Wearing his flying suit and parachute, Katsuzo Shima now entered the airplane and repeated the engine inspection, power test-run and primary control operation. The many observers on the field watched silently and a mass sigh of relief could almost be heard as Shima, evidently satisfied, lifted his head from studying the control panel. He raised his left hand and rapidly swung it from side to side, signalling the ground crew that he was ready to try a ground run. The mechanics released the wheel chocks and slowly, for the first time, the new aircraft rolled forward under its own power.

Scores of eyes anxiously followed the gentle rolling motion of the fighter, as it taxied along the turf. The inert metal was now alive and, if everything continued to go well, it would soon soar into the air.

Shima began his taxiing tests at half past four. He ran the fighter straight ahead, dropped the speed to a crawl, and then ran swiftly down the field. He turned left and right, and made both gradual and sudden stops with the brakes. During the taxiing tests, Shima constantly noted the operation of the various flight and engine controls.

Shima returned to the starting line where the mechanics and the design team eagerly awaited his reports. The brakes had not responded to the pilot's satisfaction and the ground crew made immediate adjustments.

Again the aircraft went through the taxiing tests, this time passing them perfectly.

The fighter was ready to take wing. At exactly five-thirty it surged forward from the eastern end of the airfield with a sudden burst of engine power. Everyone focused his attention on the silver plane accelerating along the runway. The tail lifted and the plane rolled on the two main wheels. Suddenly it appeared to kick slightly, and the next moment the fighter floated into the air. The multitude of observers let out their pent-up breath as the silver ship soared just above the ground.

Shima flew the fighter on a straight and level course, maintaining a height of thirty-three feet for a distance of 550 yards. Gently he brought the aircraft back to the ground, landing softly and easing the fighter to a smooth stop. He turned and taxied back to the starting line.

The company's first jump-flight test was successful. The designers jubilantly congratulated one another, and the observers were caught in the contagion of the moment. The breath of life had been blown into Horikoshi's brain child, and Shima was cheered lustily for his performance.

The jump-flight revealed a few minor defects. The brakes especially proved inadequate, notably that on the left

Mitsubishi A6M5 (front view): this is perhaps the best angle from which to appreciate the superb economy of design exemplified in the Zero.

wheel which gave the pilot trouble in landing. Oil temperature during the short flight rose beyond its normal operating range. Otherwise the aircraft checked out perfectly, and was hailed as a complete success.'

From this point on events moved forward swiftly. The 12-*Shi* showed a tendency to vibrate beyond all estimates; the problem disappeared when a three-bladed propeller replaced the original two-blade unit installed in the prototype. After a series of more severe test flights, the navy on 14th September 1939 officially accepted the Mitsubishi 12-*Shi* fighter, applying its military designation of A6M1 Type O Carrier Fighter. By 18th October a second prototype had passed the Mitsubishi acceptance tests and was turned over to the navy; on the 25th of the month this aircraft also was accepted, as the second A6M1 fighter. Both A6M1 prototypes carried two 7.7mm machine guns above the engine, firing through the propeller, as well as a 20mm cannon in each wing, firing outside the propeller disc.

The third aircraft off the line was named the A6M2, and was fitted with a new engine the Nakajima NK1C *Sakae* 12 of 950 horsepower. With the new 14-cylinder twin-row radial, only slightly heavier than the original engine, the A6M2 passed by a healthy margin the same performance figures that only a few months before had been considered impossible.

Constant testing with the prototypes revealed still further minor difficulties in the aircraft - problems by no means unexpected in a fighter design so drastically different from anything ever produced in Japan or, for that matter, anywhere in the world. Stability-difficulties resulted in a modification to the control system, after which pilots reported the machine was a 'sheer delight' to fly. The brakes and landing gear systems were modified to make them more reliable. The ailerons were modified to increase rolling response at low speeds. As the tests continued, more and more comparisons were flown against foreign fighters, notably the Heinkel He-112 (He-100), Seversky P-35, and Chance-Vought V-143. The results were overwhelmingly in favor of the A6M1 which, the test pilots reported, exceeded by a wide margin any other aircraft in controllability and maneuverability.

Then, on the 11th March 1940, disaster struck. With Test Pilot Okuyama at the controls in a flight from Oppama Airfield, the second A6M1 aircraft disintegrated in the air, killing its pilot.

The eye witnesses' reports indicated that the aircraft had disintegrated

49

A line up of the first of the more heavily armed type of Zero, the A6M5c

during a steep dive. 'Okuyama started his first dive from a height of 3,400 feet,' noted the report, 'and pulled out safely at 1,600 feet. He climbed again to 4,900 feet and entered his second dive at approximately a 50-degree angle. The aircraft descended for an estimated 1,500 feet when suddenly a loud engine sound was heard. We could see no indication that Okuyama was pulling out; almost immediately after the engine roar we heard a sudden explosion. Instantly the aircraft disintegrated, and the scattered pieces tumbled toward the ground. No sooner had the pilot bailed out (it is more than likely, however, that he was killed in the explosion which hurled the body clear of the aircraft) than the parachute opened. At an estimated height of 1,000 feet above the sea the pilot's body separated from the parachute and plunged into the water. We believe that Okuyama died in the explosion, and that the parachute opened accidentally.'

No one could ever know for certain what had failed. Okuyama was dead, the fighter had been ripped to pieces. After an exhaustive investigation, including wind-tunnel tests, the navy concluded:

'Presumably the elevator mass-balance failed prior to the accident; we believe that shock loads exerted on the aircraft during landings caused this breakage. When the aircraft commenced its dive and accelerated, it

is possible that elevator flutter started, creating throughout the aircraft severe vibrations which led to complete disintegration.'

The accident, which the engineers felt they had identified accurately, placed only a temporary damper on developing the new aircraft as an operational machine. Even further impetus was felt at Mitsubishi when bomber losses in China began once again to soar, as the Japanese struck deeply into enemy territory, where they could not be defended by escort fighters.

Fighter pilots serving in China sent home urgent requests for the new Mitsubishi of which they had heard so much. 'The fighter's outstanding performance fired the pilots with enthusiasm,' noted Masatake Oku-

miya, 'and they yearned to test its capabilities against enemy fighters. The operational groups were willing to accept the new aircraft as soon as the specific cause of the second prototype's destruction had been corrected. They felt they could cope with any further difficulty which the aircraft might present; and they further stated that defects were a secondary matter if only the Navy would guarantee the A6M2 fighter's announced speed and range.'

Excitement swept through the engineering and fighter pilot units working on the new fighter. The development program went into a day-and-night, seven-days-a-week schedule.

Crucible

Every available fighter was hurled into the accelerated test program. Mitsubishi and navy test pilots punished the aircraft in series of maneuvers intended to subject the new machine to the severest stresses of aerobatic flight, the same kind of maneuvers they might have to perform in combat. As quickly as the elevators were modified on all A6M aircraft and other changes made, as determined by the testing program, the navy rushed the test models into simulated combat-firing tests. Between 10th and 24th June 1940 Lieutenant Shimokawa and his pilots of the Yokosuka Air Corps made a series of armament tests with the 20mm cannon, during which, under different stresses of flight, they fired 2,396 explosive shells. The pilots discharged their cannon under many flight attitudes, including steep turns, with an acceleration factor of up to 5G. They made steep descending turns with wing loads up to 5.5G, through loops up to 5.5G, straight and level flight, diving and climbing. Through all the maneuvers the heavy wing cannon were fired to subject the wing to brutal loads. The main sys-

tems passed all tests perfectly, but Mitsubishi decided to modify the shell and link ejector chutes of the cannon to increase their reliability.

Test pilots moved quickly into high-altitude tests, the first of which was made on 25th June. The fourth prototype (despite lack of adequate fuel pressure) climbed to 19,685 feet in 9 minutes 18 seconds; to 26,247 feet in 14 minutes 30 seconds; and to 32,808 feet in 28 minutes 7 seconds. At 33,792 feet, after 34 minutes and 25 seconds of steady climb, the test pilot started earthward. He complained that with full engine performance he could have flown considerably higher. Engineers discovered the problem arising from excessive vaporization of fuel (vapor lock) which blocked the fuel lines and reduced engine power. Changing the fuel to a special 92-octane grade eliminated the problem.

By 15th July the accelerated engineering flight tests were completed, and the Japanese navy decided it was time to toss tradition out of the window. The many engineering modifications still to be made would require several months to elapse before

Claudes and Zeros parked at the Mitsubishi factory in Nagoya

the machine could be officially adopted as an operational, or service, aircraft. But to follow established routine would delay the despatch of the fighter to China, and the demands for the new machine were becoming louder with every passing week. On the 21st July 1940 the navy showed just how strong it felt those demands were.

Two newly organized fighter squadrons (*Hikotais*), comprising fifteen pre-production A6M2 fighters under the command of Lieutenant Tamotsu Yokoyama and Lieutenant Saburo Shindo, departed from Japan for the Asiatic mainland. Two Mitsubishi G3M (Type 96) Nell bombers functioned as navigational mother aircraft during the long ferry mission. Preceding the fighters was a team of engineering and maintenance experts. When they arrived at Hankow they immediately started training mechanics and establishing spare parts stores and facilities for the new A6M2 aircraft.

Just how much of a risk was being taken may be better understood when we realize the new engines were still not performing to the complete satisfaction of the navy. The *Sakae* 12 engine suffered from an excessive temperature rise in the engine cylinders; fortunately, the mechanics at Hankow were able almost at once to eliminate the problem. The pilots also reported difficulty in releasing the auxiliary fuel tank slung beneath the belly, especially when flying faster than 207 mph. 'The operational veterans,' reported Okumiya, 'considered this of secondary performance, since they felt that their superior skill and the excellent performance of the aircraft would overcome the disadvantage of combat with the tank still attached.'

As soon as they arrived in China the A6M2 pilots flew familiarization flights and attended to the minor modifications required.

On the last day of July 1940 the navy officially adopted the 12-*Shi* project as a regular service aircraft, and, in commemoration of the 2,600th Japanese Calendar Year (AD 1940), desig-

nated the new machine as the A6M2 Type O Carrier Fighter Model 11.

The Zero fighter was now a reality.

A Japanese fighter pilot described his initial reaction to the Zero in this way:

'I was in for a tremendous surprise. On the airfield I saw strange new fighter planes, as different from the familiar A5M Claudes as night from day. These were the new Mitsubishi Zero fighters, sleek and modern. The Zero excited me as nothing else had ever done before. Even on the ground it had the cleanest lines I had ever seen in an aircraft. We now had enclosed cockpits, a powerful engine, and retractable landing gear. Instead of only two light machine guns, we were armed with two machine guns and two heavy 20mm cannon as well.

The Zero had almost twice the speed and range of the Claude, and it was a dream to fly. The aircraft was the most sensitive I had ever flown, and even slight finger pressure brought instant response. We could hardly wait to meet enemy planes in this remarkable new aircraft.'

Sixteen months before the attack on Pearl Harbor, the Zero fighter flew its first combat mission. The date was 19th August 1940. But the Japanese hopes for a baptism by fire of the new Zero failed to materialize.

The enemy refused to fight.

On the 19th August, Lieutenant Tamotsu Yokoyama led an escort formation of twelve Zeros, protecting a force of some fifty bombers, on a strike against Chungking. There was no opposition.

The next day, the 20th, Lieutenant

peared over Chungking, weaving slowly over bombers that dropped their explosives with methodical precision. And again, for the third time, the Chinese fighters failed to appear. This time the Japanese were determined to rouse the hornets from their nest. The Zeros swooped down from their escort altitude and shot up airfields and ground installations. They were – literally – daring the enemy to fight. Still the Chinese refused to be drawn.

The next day thirteen Zeros and their bombers were back, and once more the Chinese laid low as the bombers pounded and battered their objectives. The Zero pilots were pulling every trick they knew to draw the enemy into a fight. With the bomb runs completed the Japanese formations wheeled to leave the area. Long minutes later, flames crackling in the city and smoke billowing upward for thousands of feet, a Japanese reconnaissance plane appeared over the city, far above visual sight. The Japanese crew searched the area with binoculars. One man pointed and reached for his radio microphone. Moments later the Zero pilots received the word they wanted – Chinese fighters were over the city, preparing to land at their home fields. Immediately the Zeros swung back toward Chungking, going for altitude. They arrived over the city with the sun directly behind them in a classic situation to bounce.

And bounce they did. Thirteen Zeros came out of the sun in long, slanting dives to hit the Chinese like a collapsing brick wall. Twenty-seven Russian fighters, a mixture of Polikarpov I-15 biplane and I-16 monoplane fighters (the I-16s were considerably faster than the older Claudes, but outclassed in speed by the Zeros), milled around in terror and confusion, their Chinese pilots helpless before the slashing attack.

In a wild fight that lasted thirty minutes the Zero pilots cut their enemy to pieces. The battle ended with every Chinese fighter shot down –

Saburo Shindo flew an identical mission, twelve Zeros escorting fifty bombers, against the same city. Despite the fact that for two successive days the Japanese bombers wrought havoc among their targets, Chinese fighters still refused to defend the city.

The military leaders in Japan were extremely enthusiastic about the first two missions. Although there had been no actual combat engagement the Zero fighters had initiated a revolution in fighter operations. A total of twenty-four new fighters had flown a round trip of more than 1,150 miles nonstop – a performance considered by European and American engineers to be 'impossible'.

Three weeks went by without action. On the 12th September another force of twelve escorting Zeros ap-

Above and below: The opposition to Japanese fighters in the China theatre –
Russian-built Polikarpov I-153 biplane and I-16 monoplane fighters.
Right: Two of the types of Japanese offensive aircraft escorted by the Zero –
the Aichi D3A Val dive bomber and the Nakajima B5N Kate torpedo bomber

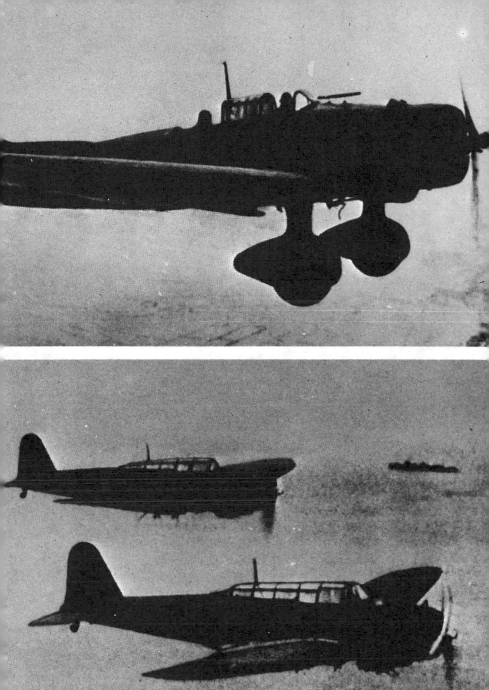

a stunning testimonial to the quality of the Zero and the skill of its pilots.

Not one Zero fighter was lost.

Flight-Officer Koshiro Yamashita overnight became a national hero in Japan. In the swirling air battle his guns and cannon shot five enemy fighters out of the air, giving Yamashita the status of an 'ace' for a single combat engagement. Although the Japanese had shot down every enemy fighter they encountered, the Zero pilots found they could claim only twenty-two planes among them for victory credits. Two of the Russian fighters collided in the mêlée and plummeted into a mountainside. Three more fighters went out of action when their pilots, not under attack but their courage demolished, bailed out of their fighters in panic.

Sticking to the old adage of striking while the iron is hot, that same afternoon a large force of Aichi 99 'Val' dive bombers, without fighter escort, flew from Ichang airbase to strike again against Chungking. They were unopposed by enemy fighters. Two days later, on the 15th September, 'Kate' attack bombers caused

tremendous damage within the city. And again there was no attempt to ward off the Japanese raiders.

The Japanese stuck to their guns, aiming to attack the enemy wherever he could be found. On the 4th October eight Zeros shepherded twenty-seven bombers in a very long range strike against Chengtu in Szechwan province in an effort to rouse the Chinese from their prime air base. The Chinese again refused to leave the ground. The Zero pilots, knowing that the Chinese would not expect any delays from the Japanese fighters at such long range, made a wide swing around the target, slipped down through broken clouds and exploded among unsuspecting Chinese pilots flying at Taipingssu airfield. Before the stunned Chinese could scatter five Russian fighters and one Russian bomber were going down in flames, again without loss to the Zeros.

The victory took on even greater import when a reconnaissance plane brought home photographic proof of nineteen hulks on the ground – planes strafed and burned out by the Zeros.

This was the pattern that followed

Ground crew wave off a unit of
shore-based A6M2 Zeros

wherever the Zero fighters made their appearance in China. There would be a brief and furious encounter with the wicked new Japanese fighter, brutal losses sustained by the Chinese, and from then on absolute Japanese air superiority. Writing of the October strikes with the Zeros, Masatake Okumiya noted that as a 'consequence of these attacks, the backbone of Chinese air strength in the Chungking and Chengtu areas was broken. For weeks afterward the skies over these two cities were conspicuously free of enemy planes.'

By the end of 1940 the Japanese, in the combat debut of the Zero fighter, had placed an aggregate of 153 of the new fighters over enemy targets. Fifty-nine Chinese planes had been shot down in air-to-air battles; forty-two Chinese planes had been destroyed in strafing attacks; Zeros lost in combat: none.

Through the early months of 1941 a small force of Zero fighters carried the brunt of offensive air operations against the Chinese. The general pattern of aerial combat remained unchanged. Slowly the Chinese built up their replacement fighter strength, and then hurled a powerful fighter force at the Japanese. But the pattern remained the same, as the Zeros tore apart whatever new forces were thrown against them.

On 14th March 1941 twenty-four Chinese fighters rained from the skies over Chengtu, burning or shot to wreckage. Again the Zeros emerged from the great air battle without a single loss.

Not until 20th May did the Japanese lose the first Zero, and even here the Chinese could not claim a victory in aerial combat. A force of Zeros strafing Taipingssu and Shuanglin airfields in the Chengtu area ran into an unexpected storm of blistering anti-aircraft fire. The Zero flown by Chief Flight Petty-Officer Kimua took heavy strikes and burst into flames, exploding as it struck the ground. More than a month later, on a low-altitude flight between Lanchow and Yuncheng, the second and last Zero to be lost in combat prior to the

Second World War went down under a withering barrage of flak.

What combat was like from the point of view of the Zero cockpit is related by Saburo Sakai:

'On August 11th, 1941 I was assigned to a mission with the express purpose of forcing the enemy into a fight. It was an 800-mile nonstop flight, from Ichang to Chengtu . . . On our penetration flight we escorted seven twin-engined Mitsubishi Type 1 'Betty' Hankow shortly after midnight, and we picked them up over Ichang. The night was pitch black, and our only landmark was the whitish Yangtze Valley winding its way across the dark country. We arrived at Wenkiang airstrip before dawn, circling slowly until daybreak. Finally the sky lightened. No enemy fighters appeared. We watched the flight leader bank his Zero and dive. That was the signal to strafe.

One after the other we plummeted from the sky toward the airfield, where I saw Russian fighters already moving along the runways on their takeoff runs. Their ground crews were running frantically over the field, heading for the trenches.

I pulled out at low altitude, coming up behind one E-16 [or I-16] fighter as it rolled down the field. It was a perfect target, and a short cannon burst exploded the fighter in flames. I flashed across the field and spiraled sharply to the right, climbing steeply to come around for another run. Tracers and flak were to left and right of me, but the Zero's unexpected speed threw off the enemy gunners.

Other Zero fighters dove and made strafing passes over the runways. Several of the Russian fighters were burning or had crashed. I pulled out of a dive to catch another plane in my sights. A second cannon burst and there was a mushrooming ball of fire.

There was nothing left to strafe. Our attack had cleared the field of enemy planes, and not a single Russian aircraft was able to fly. The majority either were burning or had exploded. Back at 7,000 feet, we noticed the hangars and other shops burning fiercely from the regular bombing attack. It was a thorough job. We were disappointed in the lack of air opposition, and continued to

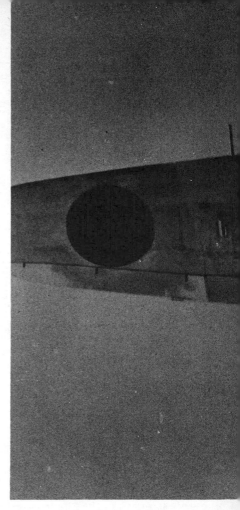

circle, hoping the towering smoke would draw the enemy planes.

Three Zeros suddenly dropped out of formation and raced for the earth. Far below me I saw a brightly colored biplane hedge-hopping over the ground. In a flash the three fighters had jumped the enemy plane, hurling bullets and cannon shells without success as the skilful enemy pilot rolled right and left, snapping his slow but agile plane through wild gyrations to evade the slugs and shells. All three fighters screamed up and away from the unscathed biplane.

Now it was my turn, and I caught the biplane dead in my sights and squeezed the trigger. He was gone, rolling violently off to the left, cutting around in a turn too sharp even for

the Zero to follow. Another Zero joined the fray, and the five of us slewed desperately through the air to catch the elusive enemy in our sights. That pilot was an absolute master. The biplane was almost like a wraith as it snap-rolled, spiraled, looped, and turned through all sorts of seemingly impossible maneuvers. We were completely unable to catch him in a solid burst.

Then suddenly we neared the summit of a low hill west of Chengtu. The biplane pilot had no choice but to clear over the hill, slow-rolling as he climbed. It was the one mistake, the one fatal error which no pilot is allowed. His belly flashed before my sights, and the cannon shells tore through the floorboards into the

Zero shows off the details of its underbelly

cockpit. The biplane fell off into a wide spin, even as another Zero threw useless shells into the ship with a dead man at the controls. It crashed into a hill and exploded.'

The total of battle engagements of the Zero fighter in China makes ridiculous the contention that the Japanese had been keeping their star aerial weapon concealed from Allied eyes prior to the onset of war across the Pacific. There were American, Russian, British, French and other Allied observers in China. The Zeros carried out seventy separate missions, including bomber escort, fighter sweeps, and low-level strafing attacks.

The Japanese put an aggregate of 529 Zero fighters directly over the Chinese cities, on missions that at times ranged 1,200 miles non stop. They shot down ninety-nine Chinese fighters confirmed, in addition to damaging many more.

As has been mentioned earlier, while the Japanese never lost a Zero to enemy aircraft, two of the new Mitsubishis were shot down by ground fire, and whatever was left in the form of wreckage fell into Chinese hands, and thus might have been seen by Western observers.

The impact of the Zero fighter – in China and for the coming air war across the Pacific – was extraordinary. General Okumiya provides a summary:

'In late August and early September of 1941, their missions accomplished, the China-based bombers reported to new stations in both Japan and Formosa. During their second combat tour of four months, we placed 2,600 bombers over enemy targets. Of this number, we lost only one bomber, and that aircraft fell to enemy anti-aircraft fire. In the dozens of raids which the bombers carried out, they encountered only ten Chinese fighter planes which managed to slip past the escorting Zero fighters. Even so, the enemy fighter planes failed to destroy any of our bombers *or* fighters.

These facts demonstrate clearly the Zero's effectiveness in the China campaign. Where once we had reached the point of prohibitive bomber losses to enemy fighters and anti-aircraft [fire], the arrival of the Zeros destroyed the enemy planes' effectiveness as interceptors. In summation: the Zero gave us undisputed command of the air over both our own territory and that of the enemy.'

As the final clash between Japan and the United States, along with the other Allies, became more and more inevitable, the Japanese rushed ahead with their preparations for the war they felt must come. The Zero fighter, obviously, was one of the more critical of the many elements of this preparation.

Despite the resounding success of the Zero in China, it represented a drastic breakaway from design tradition and, accordingly, could not hope

to avoid many teething and development problems. There were also certain inherent faults in the design, weaknesses little apparent in China because of the combat conditions encountered there, but which became very obvious in the Pacific as the tempo of the air war quickened, and the quality of the aircraft contesting the Zero continued to improve.

For example, the Zero fighter series was never completely free from one of the most loudly voiced complaints of its pilots, poor aileron control at high speeds. The effect was as if the controls had stiffened to the point where the pilot could hardly roll the fighter. Below an indicated airspeed of 150 mph, slow barrel rolls could be performed with ease and were, in fact, one of the better features of the Zero. But when the indicated airspeed went up to 180 mph, the aileron control became sluggish. Above 230 mph aileron control became so heavy the fighter could not even be held in a slow barrel roll. This weakness in performance, soon discovered by the fighter pilots contesting the Zero, led to specific tactics to overcome the Zero's unparalleled maneuverability, i.e. if one could keep one's speed high in combat, the Zero could not match one in rolling. And with a slow entry into a roll, of course, the ability to turn rapidly was impeded severely, and the Zero lost its greatest advantage – in-fighting agility.

Was this a result of poor design? Not at all, as Jiro Horikoshi explains:

'The loss in control at high speeds may be traced back to the period before the war, when our navy pilots insisted that the smallest possible turning radius in symmetrical motion should be the outstanding feature of a fighter. An additional demand of almost equal importance was that the fighter have the ability to roll rapidly in either direction at low speed.

In other words, the demand for the shortest turning radius meant that the fighter aircraft must be designed with a low wing loading and/or a large wing area, with resultant wide span. It became necessary to pay particular attention to rolling ability at low speeds, which required large aileron surfaces; these were also required to meet the demands of the Zero as a carrier fighter, where smooth and sensitive lateral control at low speeds was necessary for deck landings.

Throughout the flight tests of the prototype 12-*Shi* fighter, pilots complained of poor aileron control at high speeds. We feared, however, that a remedy for this situation would involve a sacrifice of low-speed maneuverability. Temporary measures to alleviate sluggish aileron control at high speed were undertaken, but were generally ineffective.'

No history of the Zero fighter could be complete without attention to its greatest failing, the inability to withstand heavy punishment from enemy gunfire. There is no doubt that this factor became increasingly important to the Japanese as the Pacific War went on. But the reason for this situation, the reasoning behind its existence, can be told best in the words of Horikoshi:

'Probably the greatest weakness

. . the new Mitsubishi . . . sleek and modern'

of the Zero – and every other Japanese military aircraft – was its lack of protection against enemy fire. Again, Japanese tradition had been allowed to modify our aircraft design; the military, which had been faithful to the principle "the best defense is a good offense", thought it illogical to sacrifice an airplane's striking power by the weight of armor plate and other protection.

This erroneous philosophy manifested itself in the construction of our warplanes and warships. Even our bombers, which would most often be nakedly exposed to the fury of enemy fighters, were vulnerable in this respect. It was not entirely illogical to achieve maximum performance in a fighter by sacrificing its protection of armor plating and self-sealing fuel tanks, since many thought that the resulting gain in performance would give the fighter sufficient edge over an enemy to assure its victory.

During the period when we designed the 12-*Shi* carrier fighter it appeared that no country in the world was devoting serious attention to the

protection of a fighter through heavy armor plate, effective self-sealing tanks, and other devices. By 1940–41, however, the lessons gleaned from the early air battles of the Second World War made it evident that such protection was not only advantageous to a fighter, but indispensable.

Japanese military personnel and aircraft engineers failed to heed these lessons. Considering the resources and industrial strength which Japan then possessed, the perfection of fighter protection would have required considerable time. In failing to demand fighter protection even when the events of 1940–41 had become common knowledge, the military committed an error with tragic consequences. The failure of our engineers to initiate their own investi-

gation into the matter should be regarded as a matter of negligence. The absence of official requirements is little excuse.

The policy of ignoring protection for our fighter aircraft produced a series of Japanese fighters which in the early days of the war shattered enemy opposition. Much of this opposition, it must be admitted, consisted of fighters inferior to the Zero in performance. Notwithstanding this early success, the need for armor plate and other protection was clearly evident in the reports of the effectiveness of the enemy's heavy guns against our fighters. Japan took little heed of these lessons and only when American fighters began to appear in the Pacific in ever-growing numbers were measures taken to

eliminate this defect.'

Well before the Japanese committed their destiny to the strike at Pearl Harbor and across the Pacific and Asia, steps were already under way to bring about modifications to the Zero fighter that would improve its performance and, the Japanese hoped, would continue to sustain the superiority they knew the Zero would provide for them in the opening phases of the war.

During mid-1940 the navy directed Mitsubishi to speed up the production flow of the Zero fighter, and the first mass production assembly line at Mitsubishi's Number Three airframe plant at Nagoya, in mid-Honshu, was soon turning out fighters at a steady rate. These were the A6M2 Model 11 fighters, which were produced steadily

A fine study of a shipboard model Zero incorporating folding wing-tips

while the navy and Mitsubishi continued accelerated testing of the A6M1 and A6M2 prototypes. During the testing program a wing spar failed in one Zero, and immediately corrective measures were taken to prevent its recurrence in production models. A modified wing was ordered into production and was incorporated into the Zero line, commencing with the twenty-second A6M2 Model 11 fighter. By November 1940 the company had completed production on sixty-four A6M2 Model 11 Zeros, when it shifted into manufacturing the latest version, the A6M2 Model 21 which was to be the fighter in wide use at the time of Pearl Harbor.

A Zero A6M2 Model 11 scuds through a clouded sky

During combat in China, when the Japanese were perfecting the Zero, the navy went ahead with its trials to qualify the Zero for use as a carrier fighter. With its wingspan of 39 feet 4½ inches the Zero could hardly be fitted within the elevators of carriers. Horikoshi modified the wings so that the outboard 19.6875 inches of each wingtip folded upwards. Starting with the 127th production fighter, the company installed on the ailerons new balancing tabs which were linked to the gear-retracting system; these reduced the stick force for high-speed lateral control. The production change for this model of the A6M2 Model 21 began in February 1941.

The A6M2 Model 21 fighter, which carried the brunt of Japan's fighting in the early stages of the war, had a maximum speed at optimum altitude (16,570 feet) of 332 mph, and had a demonstrated ability to climb from a standing start, under no-wind conditions, to 19,680 feet in 7 minutes 27 seconds. Its best rate-of-climb was 4,517 feet per minute. Its range of more than 1,200 miles was far superior to anything in the Allied camp.

The Model 21 Zero had a radius of turn, in a steady turn, with entry speed at 230 mph, of 1,118 feet.

At slow combat speed the fighter had a radius of turn of 612 feet.

Entering a 180-degree steep turn with an entry speed of 230 mph, the fighter could complete the turn in 5.62 seconds, with an exit speed from the turn of 188.9 mph.

The aircraft had a normal positive-G load factor of 7G, with a safety factor of an additional 1.8G. The normal negative-G load factor was 3.5G, with a safety factor of an additional 1.8G.

The wingspan was 39 feet 4½ inches and the length 29 feet 8¾ inches. Height on the ground was 9 feet 2 inches. Gross weight in combat configuration was 5,313 pounds. The engine produced 950 horsepower at its best altitude of 13,800 feet. The wing area was 241.541 square feet, the wing loading 22 pounds per square foot and the power loading 5.5 pounds per horsepower.

There are always certain variations in any particular aircraft with reference to 'exact' performance specifications, depending upon the weight of the aircraft, external modifications, and other factors. For this reason the A6M2 Model 21 is sometimes referred to as having a maximum speed of 317 mph, while engineering flight tests often showed the airplane as having a maximum speed of 327.7 mph. At times aircraft modifications that alter the performance are not visible to the eye, such as increasing the ammunition loads, which increase total weight but reduce speed and rate of climb, etc.

After producing sixty-four A6M2 Model 11 fighters, the Mitsubishi plant at Nagoya produced a total of 740 A6M2 Model 21 aircraft. This production figure is exclusive of the A6M2 Model 21 fighters turned out by Nakajima at its Koizuma factory, beginning in November 1941.

By the time Japan was ready to commit herself to full-scale war the navy had available more than 400 A6M2 fighters, most of them the Model 21 variant.

Other modifications to the basic Zero design were well under way prior to opening the Pacific War.

The navy embarked on a program to adapt the basic Zero design to floatplane operations. Operating from floats, this type of fighter could produce a measure of aerial protection for Japanese amphibious forces when neither aircraft carriers nor ground bases were available. The navy assigned to the Nakajima company the responsibility for this program, since Nakajima had extensive experience with floatplane fighters. In February 1941 Nakajima, under the company designation AS-1, began building its first prototype. The floatplane finally went into production as the A6M2-N, the 'N' indicating it was a floatplane adaptation of the basic A6M2 fighter. By April 1942 it was in mass production, and was identified also as the Type 2 Floatplane Fighter Model 11 (it was code-named 'Rufe' by the Allies). The heavy and large central float, and two mid-wing floats, reduced the aircraft's speed to 271 mph at 16,405 feet. A total of 327 floatplane Zero fighters were built at Nakajima's Koizuma factory before production ended in September 1943.

During the summer of 1941, Mitsubishi began work on a major modi-

Above: An A6M2-N floatplane fighter, a conversion of the basic wheeled aircraft by Nakajima. *Below:* The clean and economical float structure and bracing of the A6M2-N

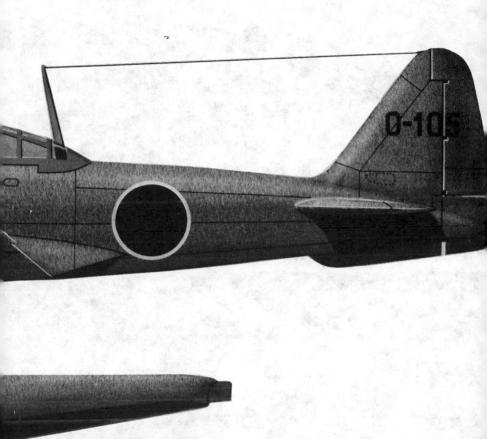

Nakajima A6M2 N (Allied code name 'Rufe')
Engine: Nakajima *Sakae* 12,940 hp at take off. *Armament:* Two 7.7mm Type 97 machine guns, and two 20mm Type 99 Model 1 Mark 3 cannon and two 132 lbs bombs. *Speed:* 270.5 mph at 16,405 feet. *Climb rate:* 16,405 feet in 6 minutes 43 seconds. *Ceiling:* 32,810 feet. *Range:* 714 miles. *Weight empty:* 4,235 lbs *Weight loaded:* 5,423 lbs. *Span:* 39 feet $4\frac{1}{2}$ inches. *Length:* 33 feet $1\frac{5}{8}$ inches

Above: A Zero made up from parts taken from five captured in New Guinea. Note the squared-off clipped wings of this model, shown also in the other example *(left)*

fication to the Zero to improve its speed, altitude, and roll-rate characteristics. This was the A6M3 fighter, which was fitted out with the 1,130 horsepower *Sakae* 21 engine, equipped with a two-speed supercharger. Initial tests showed a new top speed of 341 mph at 20,500 feet, but in almost every other respect the new fighter failed to meet the anticipated performance increases. The aircraft went into production as the A6M3 Model 32 Zero fighter and was assigned to training units and operational groups.

Complaints about the new fighter were so widespread that the Mitsubishi engineers were prompted to introduce still further changes in the aircraft to improve its performance. The Horikoshi design team removed 3.28 feet of the wingspan, by 'clipping the wings and squaring off the tips'. This eliminated the need

for folding wingtips for carrier duty and speeded up production. The maximum speed increased by almost 2 mph, but almost all other performance figures suffered slightly. The rate of climb dropped from 4,517 to 4,500 feet per minute; the radius of turn increased from 612 to 629 feet; the high-speed 180-degree turn radius increased from 1,118 to 1,155 feet, and the time required for the turn went up from 5.62 to 6.02 seconds.

The 'clipped Zero' went into combat in September 1942, carried the same armament as earlier models, and was identified as the A6M3 Model 32 fighter (code-named 'Hamp' by the Allies who listed the A6M2 fighter as the 'Zeke').

Japanese pilots found that the maneuverability of the new clipped-wing Zero suffered slightly, but the fighter was considerably faster in a dive, had ailerons more effective than the older model, and could roll better at higher speeds.

The Mitsubishi company in 1941, exclusive of Nakajima production, produced 343 of the A6M3 Model 32 fighters.

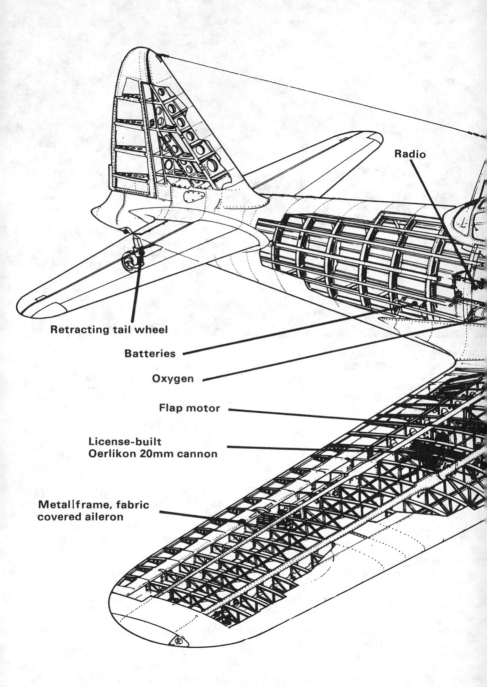

Radio

Retracting tail wheel

Batteries

Oxygen

Flap motor

License-built
Oerlikon 20mm cannon

Metal frame, fabric
covered aileron

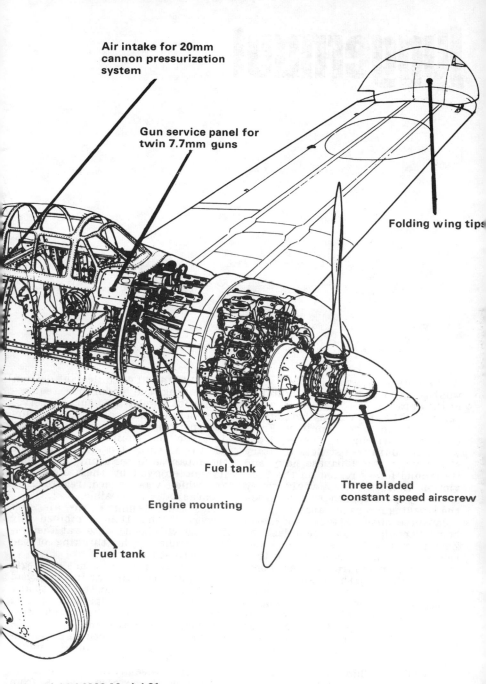

Air intake for 20mm cannon pressurization system

Gun service panel for twin 7.7mm guns

Folding wing tips

Fuel tank

Three bladed constant speed airscrew

Engine mounting

Fuel tank

Mitsubishi A6M2 Model 21
Engine: Nakajima *Sakae* 12, 925 hp. *Maximum speed:* 336 mph at 19,685 feet.
Climb rate: 4,517 feet per minute. *Ceiling:* 33,790 feet. *Range:* 1,200 miles plus.
Weight empty: 3,704 lbs. *Weight loaded:* 5,313 lbs. *Span:* 39 feet 4½ inches.
Length: 29 feet 8¾ inches

Juggernaut

At its outset, the war in the Pacific was based almost wholly on the ability of the Japanese Zero fighter to wrest control of the air over any battlefront to which it might be committed. From China to Pearl Harbor, on every front where the Japanese struck, military strategy for the Japanese navy and its ground forces rested on the conviction that the Zero would sweep aside any opposition that might wreck the invading forces of Japan.

Japanese dive, attack and level bombers could not operate unless the Zero fighter were present to sweep the skies of enemy fighters and thus leave the bombers free to press home their strikes. With a shortage of aircraft carriers relative to the scale of the operations in hand compromising Japanese plans, it was the extraordinary range of the Zero that permitted the Japanese to commit it to such extraordinary gambles. Zeros had demonstrated a non-stop range of 1,200 miles in China, while retaining sufficient fuel for thirty minutes of combat as well as a reserve for landing. Now, and in the months to come, the Zeros would be required to fly as far as 1,300 and 1,400 miles, in addition to meeting the endurance requirements for combat and for a reserve. This sensational range and endurance performance in effect gave the Japanese the equivalent of several additional aircraft carriers, and lent the Japanese forces a unique flexibility not enjoyed by their opponents and which was, indeed, regarded by them as flatly impossible.

Masatake Okumiya, the air staff officer of the 11th Combined Air Flotilla with headquarters at Kasumigaura, reflects the thinking of the Japanese at that time:

'We enjoyed one distinct strategic advantage. The air war in China had taught us clearly that the key to any successful military operation lay in command of the air. Without effective air control, our sea and land forces would at best be placed in disadvantageous positions and, indeed, might even forfeit victories which they could otherwise attain with adequate air power. It was also obvious, from past experience, that the primary means of attaining the coveted command of the air was through the

possession of a superior fighter plane.'

The purpose of this book is to review the unique position of the Mitsubishi Zero fighter plane not simply within the Japanese air arm, but also as the instrument of combat which led Japan to accept the terrible risks incurred in the slashing assaults against the United States, Great Britain and their allies.

In their studies of possible military situations the Japanese believed implicitly that a war between Japan on one side and the United States and Britain on the other would in all likelihood be decided upon the open sea. 'In the fall of 1941,' noted Okumiya, 'our army lacked aircraft capable of bombing from any base under our control the vital British installations at Singapore and similar American installations at Manila.' Equally realistic was the fact that the army had no fighter capable of matching the performance of the Zero. The army's best fighter, the Nakajima Ki-43 *Hayabusa* Oscar, although it had the same engine as the Zero, had an inferior performance. Thus the army, even if operating from

Still used alongside the Zero was the Claude, five of which are shown coming in to land after a sortie

the southernmost base in Formosa, found itself helpless to strike at American facilities in Luzon, which were considered moves indispensable to the oncoming war.

'Occupation of the Singapore and Manila installations was vital to any extension of Japanese control in the Pacific,' Okumiya observes. 'Consequently, as in the case of our operations in central and south China in the early months of the Sino-Japanese Incident, the navy was assigned the responsibility for supplying air support for our ground forces.'

Once again the plans for strategic operations rested wholly on what the Zero fighter could or could not achieve. Wherever Japan turned, it seemed, it could make no move without full and complete consideration of the role the Zero fighter would have to play. The more the Japanese studied the many different possible situations, the deeper grew their conviction that the Zero fighter was the instrument

77

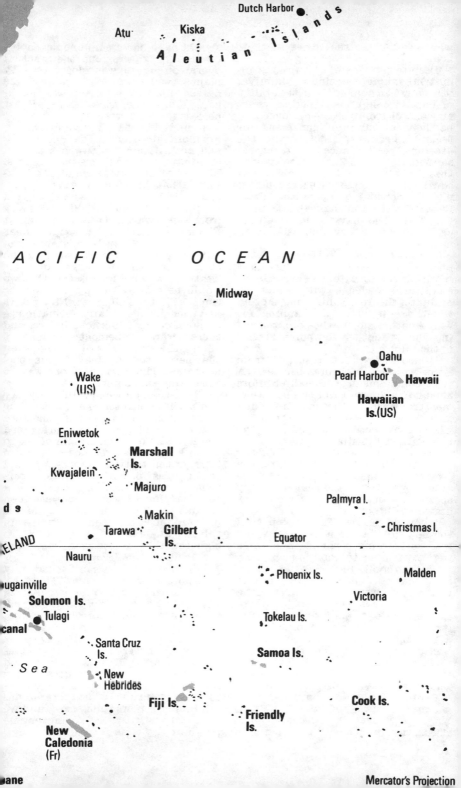

which would tip the scales in their favor.

'Despite our enemies' awesome industrial might,' continues Okumiya, 'the navy had confidence in the ability of our Zero fighter planes to wrest air control from the enemy over any battle area. Our Intelligence and our technical groups stated flatly that the excellent performance and technical superiority of the Zero fighter meant that, in battle, one Zero would be the equal of from two to five enemy fighter planes, depending upon the type. Because of this unshakeable faith in the Zero, the navy felt extremely confident of victory in initial campaigns.'

Okumiya's outlook is that of the planner and the strategist, a brilliant naval officer of extensive experience and the knowledge with which to evaluate the many different factors which are involved in planning for war. Another side of the coin, reflecting wholly another viewpoint, is that of the pilot.

Saburo Sakai had returned from China combat in September 1941. A total complement of 150 fighter pilots and an equal number of bomber crewmen transferred from the Kaohsiung airbase in China to Tainan (Formosa), where they were organised into the new Tainan Flotilla.

Sakai's viewpoint, that of the tactical airman rather than the strategic planner, is a look into the actual operations, and they lend very special meaning to the conclusions drawn by Okumiya.

'When we reached Tainan as part of the new flotilla, we began a new and intense training period. All the men were restricted to their home fields. From daybreak until late at night, seven days a week, in all kinds of weather, we were engaged in training flights to learn the finer points of escort missions, mass formation flying, strafing runs, and so forth.

Our original attack plan for the Philippines called for the use of three small aircraft carriers to bring the Zeros close to the enemy islands. They were the 11,700-ton *Ryujo;* the 13,950-ton *Zuiho,* a converted submarine tender; and the 20,000-ton *Taiho,* a converted merchant ship. Theoretically the three carriers should have had a combined capacity of ninety fighters, but their actual operation figure was closer to fifty planes, and even this number was halved on windy days. Admiral Tsukahara found the three ships almost useless for his purposes.

If, however, the Zeros could fly from Formosa directly to the Philippines and return nonstop, we could then eliminate our need for the carriers. The admiral's aides doubted, however, that a single-engine fighter could carry out a mission of such range. Clark Field was 450 miles away from our own air base, and Nichols Field, another major target near Manila, was 500 miles distant from Tainan. That meant, considering the factors of still-air range, fuel for fighting, and fuel for reserve, that we would be required to fly nonstop for some 1,100 to 1,200 miles. No fighters had ever flown – in large formations – on such combat missions before, and there were vehement arguments among the air staff as to whether even the Zero was capable of this performance. There was only one way to determine this point.

From then on we flew literally day and night to stretch the range of our planes. Apart from its range, the Zero was designed to remain in the air on a single flight for a maximum of six to seven hours. We stretched this figure to from ten to twelve hours, and did so on mass formation flights. I personally established the record low consumption of less than seventeen gallons per hour; on the average our pilots reduced their consumption from thirty-five gallons per hour to eighteen. The Zero carried a normal fuel load of some 182 gallons.

To conserve fuel, we cruised at only 115 knots at an altitude of 12,000 feet. Under normal full-power conditions, the Zero was capable of 275 knots and, when overboosted for emergencies, could reach its maximum speed of about 300 knots. On our long-range flights we lowered propeller revolutions to only 1,700 to 1,850 rpm, and eased off on the air control valve [mixture control]to its leanest mixture. This furnished us the absolute minimum of power and speed, and we hung on the fringe of losing engine power at any time and stalling.

These new long-range cruising methods extended the Zero's range by a remarkable figure, however, and our flight commanders reported the exciting news to Admiral Tsukahara, who then dropped the three small carriers from his plans. Two of them returned to Japan and one moved on to support our operations at Palau. As a result, the 11th Fleet became a fleet without any ships.'

Before the attacks on Pearl Harbor and the Philippines, no one in the Allied camp believed that the Japanese had in mass production a fighter whose performance outstripped anything that European and American designers considered possible. Even after the Zero had demonstrated its prowess time and time again, Allied war leaders refused to believe the facts. This is evident from an examination of General MacArthur's war diaries, which state that the Japanese employed several aircraft carriers in the attack on the Philippines, whereas, as we have seen from Sakai's own words, the carriers had been dispatched elsewhere by the time of the attack.

This conviction that the Japanese could not produce a fighter worthy

of the name was very common among all American military leaders. 'The unforgivable error of underestimating the enemy made by the Americans and the British,' notes Okumiya, 'was perhaps best illustrated in the reliance placed upon the antiquated Brewster F2A Buffalo fighter plane, which American aviation experts boasted was "the most powerful fighter plane in the Orient", and a "fighter plane far superior to anything in the Japanese air force". Against the Zero fighters, the Buffalo pilots literally flew suicide missions.'

As later judgments would show, the Allies were soon forced to revise their estimates.

'December 7, 1941 . . . will live as the date of one of the most brilliant military performances of all time. Superbly planned and superbly executed . . .'

'On December 7, 1941, he [the Japanese] achieved complete surprise. He struck swiftly, boldly, accurately . . . He made full capital of the paralyzing effect of his initial assault.'

'The attack achieved perfect tactical surprise . . . From the standpoint of air employment alone, his first stroke was masterful.'

These statements were not written by any Japanese historian or a neutral observer. They are from official military documents of the United States,

An important factor in the enormous and astounding range of the Zero was the large drop tank

Above: The Brewster Buffalo, no match for the more nimble Japanese fighter. *Right:* All set for the attack on Pearl Harbor, Zeros from the carrier *Akagi* run up their engines

and every one of those statements is positively and chillingly accurate.

Behind every brilliant stroke lay the overwhelming Japanese confidence that the Zero would make it possible for the other military arms to function as planned.

Even more astonishing is the fact that for combat operations on all fronts the Japanese could deploy barely 400 Zeros. If ever a nation based its war plans on a single machine, the Japanese commitment to the Zero must be the ultimate example.

Pearl Harbor does not occupy a major place in this book, for the simple reason that there were no major air battles fought at Pearl Harbor. The Japanese struck at Pearl in a two-wave attack with a total of 108 Zero fighters and 245 dive and torpedo bombers. Their plan was simple – wipe out the air defenses of of the Americans, achieve maximum air superiority as quickly as possible, and then, with minimum interference from the enemy, destroy the assigned targets.

That was the plan and its execution was as close to perfect as any military strategist could desire. In the opening strikes the Japanese destroyed or rendered useless fully half of the 300 naval planes of all types in the Pearl Harbor area. They destroyed 104 fighters and thirty-seven bombers of the Army Air Forces, tore apart hangars and other vital installations, and reduced air opposition to little more than a whisper.

'While a few enemy planes managed to get off the ground,' noted the official Japanese study of the Nagumo Task Force mission against Pearl Harbor and its environs, 'our attacking aerial forces were relatively free from enemy fighter opposition, and our fleet was now protected from an American aerial counterattack.'

Total Japanese air losses in the Pearl Harbor strike were five torpedo and fifteen dive bombers and nine Zero fighters – the first ever shot down in aerial combat. It appears impossible to determine exactly which Zeros were shot down by ground (or ship) fire and which fell to American fighters, but among the casualties to ground fire was Lieutenant Fusata Iida, a squadron leader from the carrier *Soryu*. After an air fight near Kaneohe airfield the Zeros went in low for strafing attacks. Lieutenant

A Nakajima B5N Kate torpedo bomber of the type used in the low level attacks at Pearl Harbor

Iyozo Fujita related the events thus:

'When our planes machine gunned the airfield at Kaneohe, I looked for but failed to see any anti-aircraft guns on the field. Later, however, when all the fighters assembled their formations over the field I noticed a white spray of gasoline shooting out from Lieutenant Iida's plane. There appeared to be no other damage to his fighter, and I assumed he would be able to return to the carrier.

Such was not the case, however. Lieutenant Iida circled over the Kaneohe airfield until he was sure that all our fighters were assembled in formation. Then, and only then, he closed his cockpit canopy and began to descend toward the airfield. Suddenly the Zero whipped over into an inverted position and dived vertically for the enemy positions below.

Thinking that he was going to make another strafing run on the field. I immediately began a wing-over to follow his plane down. I realized abruptly, however, that Lieutenant Iida was flying in a most unusual manner, quite different from his usual tactics. I watched the plane as it dived in its vertical, inverted position until it exploded on the ground between the Kaneohe airfield hangars.'

Not many American pilots got into the air through the hail of Japanese bullets and cannon shells, but several who did acquitted themselves brilliantly. The fighting was sparse and wildly scattered and in the brief encounters the Japanese lost both bombers and fighters to the fiercely defending American pilots.

Lieutenants Ken Taylor and George Welch each accounted for four enemy planes. No Zeros were involved. Flying Curtiss P-40B Tomahawks they took off to fly one mission, landed to refuel and rearm in the midst of blazing buildings, and rushed back into the air. This time several Aichi 99 dive bombers attacked them as they tried to take off. Welch escaped three bombers, did a wild looping maneuver out of his climb and shot a bomber off the tail of Taylor, whose P-40B was shot to ribbons in the air; Taylor barely managed to get to the ground in one piece. Both men were decorated for the destruction of the eight bombers which they had shot out of the sky.

Surprisingly, the best performance against the Zeros came from pilots flying old Curtiss P-36 Mohawk fighters of the 46th Squadron, 15th Pursuit Group, based at Wheeler Field. The American pilots were warned not to take off, since the ground gunners were shooting at anything in the sky. Disregarding the warnings the pilots climbed to 8,000 feet over Diamond Head and ran into a flock of Zeros. The odds strongly favored the Japanese – nine Zeros against five old P-36s.

The Americans caught the Japanese off balance by rushing the formation. Almost at once Lieutenants Lewis, Sanders and Phillip Rasmussen each got on the tail of a Zero and poured machine gun fire at point-blank range into their targets. Two Zeros burst into flames. Lieutenant Gordon Sterling, Jr, shot up one wildly evading Zero and then encountered the startling agility of the Japanese fighter. A Zero alongside the one being shot up by Sterling screamed through a tight loop, broke out of it directly on Sterling's tail and shot him down in flames.

Lieutenant John Thacker fought a wild encounter with the Zeros, who shot his Mohawk to ribbons. No matter what he tried to do he found a Zero pumping explosive shells into his fighter. Finally, the Mohawk a sieve from nose to tail, Thacker shoved the stick forward and ran for safety. He returned to his field with the fighter a wreck. Lieutenant Malcolm Moore fought the last battle of the dogfight. He riddled a Zero fighter, which apparently went to full power and pulled away from him, evading the Mohawk in the clouds.

Three P-40s managed to start down the runway at Bellows Field. All three were then destroyed. The first Tomahawk went into the brush at the end of the runway with a dead pilot in the cockpit. The second made it into the air – into a barrage of cannon shells from a pack of Zeros, and exploded in a tumbling, flaming mass. The third P-40B went into a tight climbing turn as the pilot, Sam Bishop, did his best to fight back. Bullets pounded into one of his legs and the P-40B almost fell apart in the air. Bishop ditched in the ocean and swam ashore.

And that ended the air fight over Pearl Harbor.

The initial air fighting in the Philippines lacked the explosive fury of Pearl Harbor. The Japanese on Formosa, honed to a fine pitch for the opening smash at American installations, found their fields closed in under heavy fog. Through the long hours of the opening night of war the fighter pilots and bomber crews waited with apprehension by their planes, listening for the American bombers they were certain would soon be there. The bombers never came. Amazed and greatly relieved, the Japanese finally climbed into their aircraft for the long flight to their targets on Luzon. The strike force was divided into several separate large formations. The Japanese knew they were in for a wild fight. The advantage of surprise had been lost. Pearl Harbor had been struck many hours before and the Americans on Luzon would be armed to the teeth and waiting to hit the incoming Japanese formations with every fighter they had.

Saburo Sakai flew in one of the large formations assigned to strike Luzon. The fighters and bombers were airborne by 1045 hours on 8th December. Fifty-three bombers and forty-five Zeros headed for Luzon; another force would be striking elsewhere, and Sakai tells us what it was like that fateful morning:

'The fighters broke up into two groups, one staying with the bombers as escorts, while the other flew ahead to tackle the interceptors, which, we felt certain, after the long delay in our attack, would be awaiting us in great strength. I flew in the first wave, and our formation moved up to 19,000 feet . . . And then the Philippine Islands hove into view, a deep green against the rich blue of the ocean. The coastline slipped beneath us, beautiful and peaceful, without another aircraft in the air. Then we were back over the China Sea.

At 1.35 pm we flashed in from the China Sea and headed for Clark Field. The sight which met us was unbelievable. Instead of encountering a swarm of American fighters diving at us in attack, we looked down and saw some sixty enemy bombers and fighters neatly parked along the airfield runways. They squatted there like sitting ducks; the Americans had made no attempt to disperse the planes and increase their safety on

Above: Only by using their superior diving speed and strength could P-40s combat the more maneuverable Japanese Zeros. *Below:* The radial-engined Curtiss P-36 Mohawk was even less a match for the Zero than the later inline-engined P-40

the ground. We failed utterly to comprehend the enemy's attitude. Pearl Harbor had been hit more than five hours before; surely they had received word of that attack and expected one against these critical fields!

We still could not believe that the Americans did not have fighters in the air waiting for us. Finally, after several minutes of circling over the fields, I discovered five American fighters at a height of about 15,000 feet, some 7,000 feet below our own altitude. At once we jettisoned the external fuel tanks, and all pilots armed their guns and cannon.

The enemy planes, however, refused to attack, and maintained their own altitude. It was a ridiculous affair, the American fighters flying around at 15,000 feet, while we circled above them. Our orders precluded us from attacking, however, until the main bomber force arrived on the scene.

At 1.45 pm the twenty-seven bombers with their Zero escorts approached from the north and moved directly into their bombing runs. The attack was perfect. Long strings of bombs tumbled from the bays and dropped toward the targets the bombardiers had studied so long in reconnaissance photographs. Their accuracy was phenomenal – it was, in fact, the most accurate bombing I ever witnessed by our own planes throughout the war. The entire air base seemed to be rising into the air with the explosions. Pieces of aircraft, hangars, and other ground installations scattered wildly. Great fires erupted and smoke boiled upward.

Their mission accomplished, the bombers wheeled about and began their return flight home. We remained as escort for another ten minutes, then returned to Clark Field. The American base was a shambles, flaming and smoking. We circled down to 13,000 feet and, still without enemy opposition, received orders to carry out strafing attacks.

With my two wingmen tied to me as if by invisible lines, I pushed the stick forward and dived at a steep angle for the ground. I selected two undamaged B-17s on the runway for our targets, and all three planes poured a fusilade of bullets into the big bombers. We flashed low over the ground and climbed steeply on the pullout.

Five fighters jumped us. They were P-40s, the first American planes I had ever encountered.

I jerked the stick, slammed rudder and spiraled sharply to the left, then yanked back on the stick for a sudden climb. The maneuver threw the enemy attack off, and all five P-40s abruptly rolled back and scattered. Four of the planes arced up and over into the thick columns of black smoke boiling up over the field, and were gone.

The fifth plane spiraled to the left – a mistake. Had he remained with his own group he could have escaped within the thick smoke. Immediately I swung up and approached the P-40 from below; the American half-rolled and began a high loop. At 200 yards the plane's belly moved into my sights. I rammed the throttle forward and closed the distance to fifty yards as the P-40 tried desperately to turn away. He was as good as finished, and a short burst of my guns and cannon walked into the cockpit, blowing the canopy off the plane. The fighter seemed to stagger in the air, then fell off and dived into the ground.

That was my third kill – the first American plane to be shot down in the Philippines.

I saw no other fighters after that, but other Zero pilots caught a group of planes in the air. Later that night, back at Tainan, our claims were for nine planes shot down, four probably destroyed in the air, and thirty-five destroyed on the ground.'

Official Japanese records show that five Zeros were missing at the conclusion of operations. One was reportedly shot down by ground fire and another four crashed on the way home from battle damage. Sakai insists that no Zero was shot down by an American fighter. The American records claim at least two Zeros shot down in battle during the air fight. The reader is left to judge for himself. However, as studies showed well after the war, many claims made in battle, and made in complete honesty, were never supported by statistical study afterward.

The other side of the story is told by the Americans. At Iba airfield a group of P-40E Kittyhawks (the P-40E, with more engine power and six .50 caliber machine guns, was a major improvement over the older P-40B Tomahawk) were preparing to swing into their landing patterns. The pilots were low on fuel and angry because they had failed to close with the Japanese. At that moment the enemy struck. Bombs exploded all about the American fighters.

The P-40E pilots slammed open their throttles and climbed in desperation to turn into the enemy, but before they could gain much speed or altitude the Zeros swarmed over them. Lieutenant Jack Donalson surprised the attackers by swinging about sharply and driving after two Zeros, damaging both fighters. This was the sum of damage – as confirmed later by Japanese reports. Before the one-sided fight ended, with Donalson providing the only real resistance, five P-40E fighters were shot down. Three other Kittyhawks later crash-landed.

At Clark Field, over which Sakai and his group circled, four P-40B Tomahawks went into the air to intercept the enemy. (This conflicts with the Japanese report of five American fighters circling at 15,000 feet, and there seems to be no way of reconciling this discrepancy.) The rest of the Japanese version of the fight – the superb bombing, the devastating strafing – is corroborated in full by the Americans. But this is not so with the air combat reports. The American records show that Lieutenant Randall Keator shot down two Zero fighters over Clark Field. The Japanese flatly deny this, insisting their records show one Zero lost in the attack, with four more going down on the long flight home.

There were other battles under way. Seversky P-35 fighters from Del Carmen were fortunate enough to gain a height advantage before being spotted by the Japanese, and the pilots dived their old fighters into a large Zero formation. With 'ridiculous ease' the Zeros turned swiftly and scattered the P-35s. To the surprise of the Japanese pilots the P-35s recovered and snarled back into the

P-35s, annihilated by the Zero

battle. What the Americans lacked in performance from their planes they made up in killer instinct. The Zeros shot the P-35s to ribbons, but by some miracle none of the Seversky fighters were shot out of the sky, although several landed as 'flying wrecks'.

'On the first day of the war,' wrote Masatake Okumiya, 'we jammed the message rooms, anxiously awaiting the initial combat reports which would inform us of initial victory, or of setbacks. Our exuberance rose steadily as an unending stream of radio messages described the courageous and amazing victories won by our naval air units. My apprehension faded with the increasing number of reported victories; incredibly, the first hours of war were totally in our favor.'

And so they were, and so they continued to be, with the Japanese using the Zero fighter with crushing effectiveness. On 10th December the pilots of intercepting P-40s did everything humanly possible to hit Japanese bomber formations; the Zeros swept in to break up every attack and the frustration of the pilots is reflected in the official records, where it is stated that the P-40s 'were overwhelmed in their attempts to break up the enemy's bomber formations'.

The experiences of other fighter squadrons were grimly similar. Ten P-40s of the 17th Squadron rushed in to attack a group of bombers protected by an estimated forty Zeros, but the American pilots failed completely to crack the aerial wall. 'Enemy fighters thwarted almost every effort,' stated the official reports, and the bombers continued their devastating strikes. Only two P-40 pilots got within shooting range of the bombers, and the Zeros soon cut them away from their targets.

Out of the ten P-40s airborne, three were shot down, without loss or even 'apparent damage' to the Zero fighters.

By the evening of 10th December the American fighter defense of the Philippines was a decimated force. The Interceptor Command could count a total of twenty-two P-40 and eight P-35 fighters for the entire Philip-

Victorious yet again, a delighted Japanese pilot describes his combat

pines, and many of these were barely fit to fly. That the US forces had no fighter defense left was made abundantly clear when MacArthur's headquarters ordered to cease all fighter combat immediately. The few remaining fighters would be used for reconnaissance only.

The Japanese continued their systematic destruction of primary targets in the Philippines, virtually unopposed.

From all the fighting there emerged only one brilliant spark, in the person of Lieutenant Boyd 'Buzz' Wagner. In the week following 13th December, when he was attacked while flying reconnaissance and ground attack missions, Buzz Wagner shot down five Zero fighters to become the first American ace of the Second World War.

Yet it was only a single flickering light of victory in an otherwise entirely gloomy episode. There were no great air battles fought in the opening days of the Pacific war. It was a one-sided show with the Japanese running rampant all the way, and Okumiya provides an evaluation:

'On the war's second day, severe storms reduced the effectiveness of our attacking planes. High winds and rain forced several fighters into the sea. On 10th December, however, a savage aerial attack effectively neutralized the Cavite Naval Base area in south Manila. Forty-eight hours later not a single enemy plane remained on Luzon Island to contest our rampaging Zero fighters. Within these three days the aerial operations against Luzon Island ceased; by the fourth day, 13th December, we dismissed the possibility of any form of enemy aerial counterattack. In three days our Zero fighters had given us absolute supremacy in this theater of war.

After the beginning of the war, we learned that, although the Zero fighter had appeared in battle in China more than a year prior to December 1941, the Allies professed astonishment at the sight of our new fighter and were caught completely unaware by the Zero's performance. Months after the Philippines campaign, the Allies still did not realize the true flight capabilities of the Zero. When Zeros raided Port Darwin, Australia, early in 1942, the enemy accepted without question the fact that the Zeros must have flown from our carriers, when in reality they flew from our newly captured land bases on Timor Island.

In every operation in December of 1941 we quickly attained numerical as well as qualitative superiority. We fully appreciated the fact that the geographical isolation of the Pacific and Asiatic battle areas would prevent the enemy from rapidly reinforcing his forces, and that by quick, decisive onslaughts we would not only achieve local air supremacy, but would retain this advantage.

Within ten days of the opening bombing attack, the enemy planes disappeared entirely from the Philippines. Our forces wasted no time in pressing their newly won gains. On 25th December, our task force swarmed ashore on Jolo Island in the southern part of the Sulu Sea and occupied its airfield. To obtain local air coverage we dispatched twenty-four Zeros of the Tainan Air Corps in a mass nonstop formation flight of 1,200 nautical miles (nearly 1,400 statute miles).

Our fighters experienced little difficulty in ridding the skies of the remaining enemy planes; by early March of 1942, our naval land-based air forces had landed in the string of South Pacific islands. Quickly the entire Dutch East Indies came under the control of our air force. The Tainan Air Corps advanced to Bali Island in the Dutch East Indies through Jolo Island, Tarakan, Balikpapan, and Bandjermasin; the 3rd Air Corps flew to Davao, Menado, and Kendari [Celebes], then divided into two groups, the first of which advanced through Makassar to Bali Island. The second group moved into Dilly on Timor Island by way of Amboina.

Under Admiral Tsukahara's command, the naval land-based air forces in the southern Pacific area definitely shot down in air combat and destroyed on the ground a total of 565 enemy planes from 8th December 1941, until the close of the Java Operation. Of this number, our Zero fighters accounted for 471 planes, or 83 per cent

**Japanese aircrew help to load
a bomb before a mission**

of the total.

We can judge the effectiveness of our Zero fighters by observing that in all our operations in the first months of the war, the Zero fighters of our land- and carrier-based air forces destroyed 65 per cent of all the enemy planes lost. This accomplishment contributed directly to the success of our operations. At Pearl Harbor, as well as in the Philippines and Dutch East Indies, we could not possibly have achieved our land, sea and air victories with a fighter plane of lesser performance than the Zero. Our entire strategy depended upon the success of this aircraft.'

Time of the Zero

In a book concerned specifically with the Zero, and its effect upon the war, rather than the war itself, the author has no choice but to select, subjectively, those incidents he feels best reflect the qualities of the Zero fighter.

Certainly, by now, some readers will have raised the question: 'But what about the Flying Tigers? So far we have not heard a thing about the American Volunteer Group, the P-40s commanded by Claire Chennault, and everyone knows they fought the Japanese for years before Pearl Harbor!'

So now is as good a time as any to deal with that subject. First, and of immediate importance, is to eliminate the myth that the Flying Tigers fought the Japanese 'for years before Pearl Harbor!' Tell the average air war enthusiast that the Flying Tigers never fought the Japanese until thirteen days after Pearl Harbor and you will have a minor war of your own on your hands. No matter; it is still the truth.

The AVG fought its first battle against a Japanese force attacking Kunming, in China, on 20th December 1941. Three days later the AVG's P-40B Tomahawks, accompanied by Royal Air Force fighters, ripped into Japanese bombers raiding Rangoon, the capital of Burma.

Now, because the early air war history in the Pacific is so heavily flavored with the exploits of the AVG, it is necessary to set the record straight on this matter. The long and short of it is that the Flying Tigers carved themselves a niche in the history of aerial warfare that will seldom be equalled, and may never be surpassed. Theirs is a tale of extraordinary heroism, and anything presented here is not intended to denigrate their achievement.

When the Flying Tigers closed the record books of their existence as a group, in the first week of July 1942, they counted a total of 286 Japanese fighters and bombers destroyed in air combat. These are confirmed kills and do not include planes known to have gone down after combat, or those that crashed into the sea. By

A Zero sideslips in to a landing

The Flying Tigers, first to have any real success against the Zero.
Above: Pilots scramble as the alarm is given. *Below left and right:* Two AVG
aces – David Hill with 16 victories and William Reed. *Right:* Commander of
the AVG – Major-General Claire Chennault

Sporting the famous 'shark mouth', a P-40 of the AVG prepares to take off from its base in China

conservative estimate another twenty or thirty enemy planes must have been shot down during this period.

To accomplish its official score of 286 aerial kills the AVG lost nine pilots killed in battle and another four missing in action, presumed to have been lost in combat, for a total of thirteen pilots lost directly to enemy action. Two AVG pilots were killed on the ground by Japanese bombs. Nine more AVG fliers met death in training or during ferrying missions.

One of the more remarkable asides to the history of the AVG is that never did the available combat strength of the group exceed a total of fifty-five fighters at any one time ready for combat.

The AVG might have been known as the Group of Aces. Bob Neale shot down sixteen planes. David 'Tex' Hill achieved a score of twelve. Bill Reed got eleven. George Burgard, Bill McGarry, Ken Jernstedt, John Newkirk, Bob Little, and Charles Older were all aces with ten kills each, plus other kills shared with fellow pilots. Many more, such as Greg Boyington, achieved ace status by shooting down five or more enemy planes.

However, the AVG did not fight its battles entirely against Japanese Zero fighters. They fought against a mixed bag of fighters and bombers that included Zeros. It also included many twin-engined bombers, and of these an unknown quantity of the aircraft were Japanese army fighters and bombers. Most of the enemy planes the Tigers fought were deployed throughout Indo-China. In the southern part of that country the Japanese gathered 200 naval and 600 army aircraft. The Japanese army, of course, did not fly the Zero. Its lead fighter at the time was the *Hayabusa* Oscar which resembled the Zero to such an extent that it was often mistaken for a Zero. And on many occasions the Tigers fought the older Mitsubishi A5M2 Claude fixed-gear, open cockpit fighters. There were, to be certain, many air fights involving the Zero fighter, but the exact number of fights and Zeros is not known now and never will be. In their first diving attack against enemy bombers on 20th December, the Tigers shot down six planes out of a formation of ten, with no losses to the AVG.

The second air fight came on 23rd December, when fourteen P-40s and sixteen Brewster Buffalos of the RAF slammed into large Japanese formations striking at Rangoon.

The initial reports showed that the AVG pilots shot down six enemy planes, and the British pilots another four.

Before we go further in our story it is pertinent here to note that combat records of the early days of the war are a nightmare for the air historian. The first AVG reports showed that two P-40s were shot down but that the pilots survived. The reports also indicated that the RAF suffered no losses in the fighting, but that several Brewsters were so badly shot up they crashed on landing. This is the report, essentially, that found its way into many historical documents.

It took a long time to unravel the snarls. The final score was considerably different. AVG pilots Hank Gilbert and Neil Martin were both shot down and killed in the battle. AVG pilot Paul Green bailed out and survived. George McMillan's fighter was 'demolished', but the records do not indicate how, nor do they say whether he bailed out or crashed.

The greatest discrepancy is in the reports about the RAF fighters. The AVG records state that none were lost, but the Royal Air Force has confirmed that five Brewsters were shot down and that their pilots were killed. Thus the tally for the first engagement over Burma comes to ten Japanese planes destroyed at a cost of five British and four American fighters lost, and seven pilots killed.

The battles waged furiously, and the AVG was on its way to setting its remarkable total of kills. A mixed force of P-40s and Buffalos cracked the whip on seventy-eight Japanese bombers and fighters in the first engagement, and then fought another thirty in a second wave. The day's score showed the RAF with claims

Late model P-40Ks lined up on their base in 1942

100

The Zero . . . brilliant but not invincible

for eight kills, and five of their own planes lost. The Flying Tigers notched twenty-eight Japanese planes shot down, for a loss of two P-40s. Both AVG pilots survived.

Through his AVG pilots, Claire Chennault proved the validity of his combat theories. Chennault concentrated on the two-fighter element in hit-and-run tactics against the Japanese. The P-40B had good speed in level flight. At low altitude it could run with the Zero, but suffered severely above 12,000 feet. And, since many of the Japanese fighters encountered by the AVG were the fixed-gear Type 96 Claudes of the navy, and the fixed-gear Type 97 Nates of the army, the Tomahawks on many occasions were much faster than their fighter opposition.

Against any Japanese fighter the Tomahawk was spectacular in a dive. It was this diving speed, and the great structural strength of the P-40B, that enabled Chennault to utilize his hit-and-run tactics so effectively. AVG pilots returned home to swear by their aircraft, shot to pieces from nose to tail, and the pilot's armor plate studded with bullets. Without that ruggedness and heavy armor plating, many AVG pilots, who took direct, heavy fire from the enemy, would never have survived.

To maneuver with the Japanese fighters, Chennault warned his men, was to commit suicide. Chennault hammered over and over the admonition: do not fight the enemy on his own terms. The trick was to use the P-40B to its best advantage – get on top, dive as fast as possible, shoot, and run. It lacked elegance, but it worked.

These tactics would hardly have been effective on long-range escort missions; obviously, one does not defend one's bombers by diving out of a battle. But for the situation confronted by Chennault, against the overwhelming odds his men faced, his tactics were vindicated in brilliant fashion. Chennault was out to stop Japanese bombers. For this purpose the attack in which a fighter struck and dived away, and perhaps climbed overhead for a second attack, was deadly.

To Chennault's credit, and to that of the men of the Flying Tigers, the Japanese made a determined effort specifically to destroy the small force of volunteers. It failed, and at severe price to the Japanese. But while the AVG could damage the enemy's thrust it could do little else, and not even the overwhelming kill ratio of the AVG could stem the enemy's steamroller assault on the ground. Despite the AVG's kill superiority, which the *Army Air Forces in World War II* lists as an 'almost incredible number', the tide of war remained clearly in favor of the Japanese.

When the AVG passed into history it was replaced by an 'interim' organization, the China Air Task Force, which itself would later form the nucleus of the 14th Air Force. The CATF continued operations in mid-1942 in China against Japanese navy and army aircraft, a large number of which were Zeros. The CATF stuck to the principles of the AVG – when fighting Zeros, hit, then run as fast as possible, and never, never (if possible, that is) try to dogfight with the nimble Mitsubishis. The impact on the war of the CATF is open to question, for they launched their aerial offensive against powerful Japanese air units with only seven bombers and about thirty flyable fighters. Despite this pitiful equipment, the CATF's objective, unlike that of the AVG, was not only to stop the attacks of Japanese bombers but also to mount strikes with its own P-40 and B-25 aircraft. At the same time the Japanese mainly army fighters and bombers, did their best to knock out the CATF. All in all, it was a wild scramble of an air war that has received little attention in the history books.

Brigadier-General Robert Scott USAF (Ret) once told the writer about a man he considered to be one of the great fighter pilots of all time. Actually, he did not specify fighter pilot – just fighter. The man was Lieutenant Dallas Clinger from Wyoming. Bob Scott, who shot down thirteen Japanese planes in Asia

Robert Scott, another American ace of the China theater

A Zero captured by the Flying Tigers and presented to the Chinese on display on a Chinese airfield

told the author: 'Clinger was another man who in years gone by in the West would have been a great gunman like Tex Hill. Only Clinger wouldn't have cared whether he was on the side of the Law, the Mormons, the Church, or Jesse James. He just wanted to fight.'

Because Clinger fought Zeros, and performed the impossible in a P-40 against Zero fighters, this brief episode deserves a place in these pages.

One of Clinger's brief combat reports describes a fight he had over Hengyang, while flying with two other P-40s:

'I was flying on my leader's wing – Lieutenant Lombard – at 23,000 feet when we saw three enemy planes down below circling. There were larger formations reported around. Just then I heard my flight leader say: "There are three stragglers – let's attack 'em." So we dived into them like mad. As I shot into the Zero on the right of the formation I saw that we were in the midst of twenty-four other Zeros, all shooting at us. I got mad and shot at every plane I could get my sights on. I think I shot one down but I was so busy I didn't see it crash.'

The combat report was signed: 'Dallas Clinger – 2nd Lieutenant – Almost Unemployed.' Robert Scott fills in the details omitted by Clinger:

'What Clinger had really done was the greatest piece of daredevil flying that any of us had ever seen. Instead of diving away from the twenty-seven ship circus as the others had done, he had stayed and fought the old-fashioned "dogfight" until the Japs just about took him to pieces from sheer weight of numbers. When they straggled home they must have been the most surprised bunch of pilots in all Japan, for this crazy American with his heavy P-40 had done everything in or out of the book. He fought right side up and upside down, from 23,000 feet to less than 1,000. As many Japs as could fill the air behind Clinger would get there and hang on while they shot; but Clinger wouldn't fight fair and stay there. In the end, he came right over the field, diving from the enemy until he had outdistanced them enough to turn; then he'd pull into

an Immelmann and come back shooting at them head-on.

He was last seen after the unequal fight skimming out across the rice paddies, making just about 500 miles per hour, with some ten to twelve Zeros following. For some reason they seemed reluctant, as though they didn't know whether to run after Clinger or leave him alone. He

RAF Buffalos on patrol in Malaya

came in for lunch with his ship badly shot up by their cannon. But he had shot down one of them.'

This throws further light on the words of Lieutenant-Commander Takeo Shibata, already noted, on the merits of maneuverability versus speed and firepower in the aircraft that would become the Zero.

'I believe, that inadequate maneu- verability in a fighter can be more than compensated for by the superior skill of its pilot. I am firmly con- vinced that I myself could train our navy fighter pilots to maintain a clear superiority over enemy fighters, even with aircraft of inferior turning radius.' Dallas Clinger proved just how right Takeo Shibata really was.

The Buffalo fighters flown by RAF pilots in company with the AVG had, at least, the rare experience of seeing the Japanese on the losing side in one engagement after the other. The other pilots, Australians, New Zealanders and those from Britain who flew Buffalos and Hurricanes in Malaya found such a sight far rarer than they liked. In sum, the Zeros made mincemeat out of their opposition at Singapore and throughout the surrounding area. Malaya was under the protection of British airpower, but no one before the first air fights dared to dream just how badly they would be whipped in the air. Gregory Board, an Australian pilot who flew a Buffalo, tells of 'Intelligence briefings almost daily by the most learned of men, who came in from the other side of the Japanese bamboo curtain, and told us the best of the Japanese fighters were old fabric-covered biplanes which wouldn't stand a chance against the Buffalos.

With this ringing promise of slaughtering the Japanese in the air should they get too big for their breeches, we concentrated on flying and learning different methods of drinking gin and tonic. We flew with absolute confidence in our prowess, and we drank hard, and we were on top of the heap, as far as we were concerned.'

The Japanese struck with their usual methodical ferocity. On the third day of combat the Zeros showed up in great numbers, Board recalls. No 21 Squadron, to which he was attached, went up to take on the Japanese fighter pilots. Of course, they ran into the unexpected: 'The entire 21st Squadron was wiped out to a man,' explained Board. 'Suddenly we realized what we really had in the Buffalo – a barrel which the Zeros could outfly, outclimb, outgun, out-maneuver and outdo in almost anything else that was in the book for a fighting aircraft.'

Board recalled a fight when thirteen Buffalo fighters scrambled to intercept a force of enemy bombers: 'It was the kind of fight you never forget. The Zeros shot eleven out of the thirteen Buffalos to wreckage in the air. One other pilot and myself were the only ones to land.'

Several days later, Board and nine other pilots went after a mixed formation of bombers and Zeros. The Japanese fighters were lax in formation discipline and the Buffalos broke through to the bombers. The Zeros hit them immediately with sledgehammer blows. Board made one diving attack, and was zooming upward in a second strike when his Buffalo shook madly from bullets fired at him by a Zero. Board hung on until the bomber he was after exploded. By then the Zeros were all over them.

'Fortunately, there were enough loose clouds around for us to hide in,' Board states candidly, 'because if you mixed it up in a dogfight with a Zero, the outcome was very clear. Very quickly you were a dead man.'

Hopes soared among the British pilots when merchant ships delivered new Hurricanes and Buffalos to their thinned-down ranks. Board and his fellow pilots received new Buffalos, and then watched in dismay as the new Hurricane pilots rushed against the Zeros with the same tactics they had used against German fighters in Europe. They could have written the end before it happened – as the Hurricane pilots broke formation to mix it up in loose dogfights, the Zeros scrambled over them and shot them down in droves.

Board and ten other pilots went up in their replacement Buffalos to hit a giant formation of more than one hundred Japanese bombers and their fighter escorts. The Australians had the rare opportunity to climb to 25,000 feet, well above the Japanese formation, so that they could dive into the battle. Board had been waiting for this chance for days. He rammed the throttle to the firewall, pushed forward on the stick and dove. On his way down he tore right through the fighters, lined up his sights on a bomber and held down the trigger until the big plane exploded into large flaming chunks. It was Board's third kill. He came out in a bone-crushing zoom until he was again high above the enemy formations. A Zero appeared beneath him and Board half-rolled, hauling the stick back sharply. The Buffalo

Successful in Europe against the Germans and Italians, RAF Hurricanes (above) and Spitfires found themselves outflown by the agile Zero

The last sight seen by many an Allied airman — a Zero turns in on full throttle

hurtled out of the sky but Board never fired a shot – a Zero had latched on to his tail and the world went to pieces under him.

The instrument panel erupted in his face. Instinct made him hunch down in his seat and the move saved his life. Japanese bullets crashed off the armor plate and exploding cannon shells tried to drive the plating right through him. Without that armor he would have been killed instantly. He said it was like a bad dream in slow motion or attending your own funeral.

The Zero shot the surface of the Buffalo's wings off until Board could see the naked ribs beneath. He could feel the fighter coming apart under his hands. Frantic, he went wild, trying every trick he knew in the Buffalo to shake his pursuer.

'But whoever was in that Zero was good, damned good,' Board recalled grimly, 'and he had a hell of a better aircraft under his hands. He chopped that Brewster into ribbons . . . I had nothing left but to try and get out by going straight down. I was pulling all the power the aircraft had and I shoved the stick forward and tried to save my life by diving vertically.'

It did not work. The Zero was a nightmare glued to his tail, snapping out short, neat bursts that continued to chop away at the Buffalo. Board felt the heat as the fighter exploded into flames. The fuel tanks belched fire. Ammunition exploded in the wing racks. Acrid fumes filled the cockpit, choking the Australian. He had just enough time to plunge into a cloud where he chopped power and pulled up the nose to slow down; he rolled onto his back and released the hatch. Flames thundered into the cockpit and then he was gone, into the blessed relief of cool air. He fell for long seconds, far clear of the battle, before he pulled his ripcord to open the parachute.

Did it get any better? Not according to Board; with other pilots he barely escaped with his life on 10th February by scrambling aboard a British cruiser evacuating Singapore. The warship raced for . Java where a desperate fight was being waged against the Japanese.

Gun camera photograph of a Zero

114

'It didn't last long,' Board recalled. 'The Zeros just tore us apart. Everything sort of melts into a blur after that. We got out of Java one step ahead of the Japanese and made it to India. Here we tried to get back into fighters, but there weren't any . . . No one knew where or when we would stop the Japanese.'

Malaya . . . Sumatra . . . and then Java. One long trail of defeat marked the route for the defenders. The hard facts had sunk in everywhere. The Zeros were whipping everything which rushed into the air against them. Japanese fighters not only ripped the ranks of P-40s, Buffalos, Hurricanes and other fighters, they caught dozens of British bombers – Blenheims, Hudsons and Wildebeestes – in the air and wrought havoc among them.

Except for the success of Claire Chennault's Flying Tigers, the air war was a staggering one-sided affair. Over Darwin in northern Australia, twelve P-40s dived from high altitude into a large bomber force escorted by Zeros. The Mitsubishi pilots tore against the P-40s, whose pilots swung around to dogfight with the enemy. Eleven P-40s fell burning or broken from the sky in seconds.

The British had tried to stem the tide of the Zeros with new Buffalo and Hurricane fighters. Now they rushed a crack Spitfire group from England, complete with pilots experienced in air combat over Europe. The Spitfire had already been acclaimed as perhaps the finest close-in fighter of all time. Certainly it could cut circles inside the Luftwaffe's best, the Me-109E, in a free-for-all dogfight. Even Claire Chennault admitted that 'the Spitfire was far superior to the P-40 as a combat plane'.

But the rulebook across the Pacific was clear. Never dogfight with the Zero. The Spitfire pilots came over to rewrite the rules. They had the best fighter in the world, or so they thought.

But the Japanese had the measure of them. In only two raids the Zero pilots shot down seventeen out of twenty-seven Spitfires, losing only two of their own number.

'It was simply a matter of tactics,' Claire Chennault said later. 'The RAF pilots were trained in methods that were excellent against German and Italian equipment but suicide against the acrobatic Japs.'

On 19th February 1942 a force of twenty-three Zero fighters of the Tainan and Kaohsiung Wings took off from Balikpapan, on the east coast of Borneo, on a fighter sweep against Surabaja. A fast reconnaissance aircraft flew as navigator/pathfinder for the Zeros during the 430-mile flight. The main Japanese force reached Surabaja at 1130 hours, cruising at 16,000 feet.

That day marked one of the wildest air fights of the early phases of the Pacific War. Saburo Sakai, who flew a Zero in that struggle, relates the details:

'The enemy force anticipating our arrival was unprecedented. At least fifty Allied fighters, flying at about 10,000 feet, maintained a large, counterclockwise sweep over the city. The enemy planes extended in a long line, composed of three waves of V groups which outnumbered us by more than two to one.

Upon sighting the enemy fighters, we jettisoned our tanks and climbed for altitude. Sighting our force, the Allied fighters broke off their circular movement and at full speed closed toward us. They were prepared and eager for a fight – unlike the American fighters we had encountered over Clark Field on 8th December.

Less than a minute later the orderly formations disintegrated into a wild, swirling dogfight.

I watched a P-36 scream toward me, then flicked into a swift left roll, watching for the enemy's reaction. Foolishly, he maintained his course. That was all for me, and I snapped around into a sharp right turn, standing the Zero on her wing, and came out directly on the tail of the startled P-36 pilot.

A look behind me showed my own plane clear, and I closed the distance to the enemy fighter. He rolled to the right, but slight control movements kept the Zero glued to his tail. Fifty yards away I opened up with the guns and cannon. Almost immediately the right wing broke off and

To the Allies in the Pacific, the face of destruction . . . .

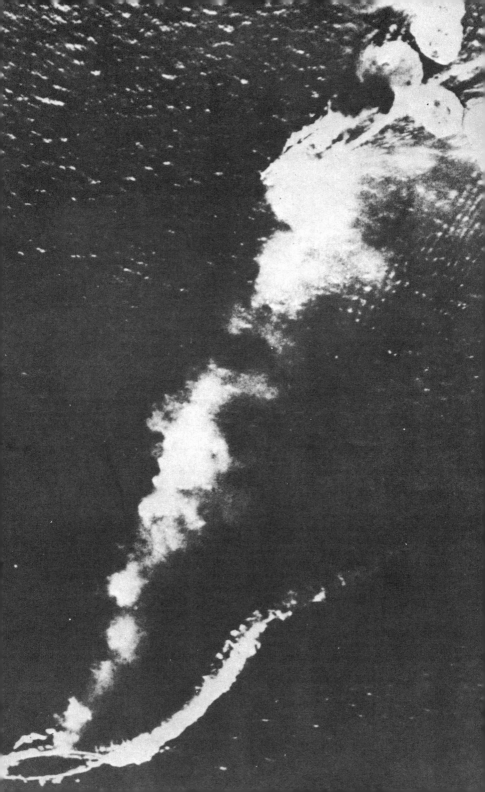

snapped away in the airstream; then the left wing tore loose. Spinning wildly, the P-36 broke up into wreckage as it plummeted. The pilot failed to get out.

Swinging into a wide, climbing turn I headed back for the main fight. At least six planes were falling in flames. Fighters swirled crazily about in the air and abruptly the olive drab of a P-36 rolled toward my own fighter. I turned to meet his rush, but in the next moment another Zero whipped upward in a steep climb, caught the P-36 in a long cannon burst, then snapped away as the Dutch plane exploded.

To my left a P-40 closed in on the tail of a fleeing Zero, and I turned desperately to draw the enemy fighter off. There was no need to do so; the Zero whipped up and around in a tight loop which ended exactly above and behind the P-40. The guns and cannon hammered and the P-40 burst into flames.

Another P-40 flashed by, trailing a streamer of flame fully three times as long as the fighter. A P-36 flipped crazily through the air, its pilot dead at the controls.

Below me, our unarmed pathfinder flashed by, caught by three Dutch fighters. The Japanese pilot was corkscrewing violently to evade the enemy tracers which flashed all about his plane.

Again I arrived too late. A Zero plummeted down in a power dive, and his cannon shells exploded the top Dutch fighter's fuel tanks. Pulling out of the dive, the Zero flashed upward in a steep zoom, catching the second P-36 from beneath. It fell off on one wing even as the third pilot whipped around to meet the Zero. Too late; his cockpit erupted in a shower of glass.

The other Zero pulled alongside my plane, the pilot waving and grinning broadly, then dropped away as he escorted reconnaissance out of the area.

A P-36, apparently fleeing the fight, passed over me. I slammed the throttle on overboost and yanked the stick

The British capital ships *Repulse* and *Prince of Wales* under air attack just before their sinking

back, looping to come out close to the Dutchman. Still climbing, I opened up with the cannon. Too soon; the pressure of the turn threw off my aim.

The cannon gave me away; the P-36 jerked hard over in a left roll and dove vertically for the ground. I cut inside his turn and went into a dive as the Curtiss flashed by less than fifty yards away. My finger snapped down on the button, and the shells exploded in the fuselage. Thick black smoke belched back. I fired two more bursts, then pulled out as a sheet of flame enveloped the Dutch fighter.'

The tenor of the war began to slow down as the Japanese accomplished their objectives. There were, to be sure, many incidents of fierce defensive fighting, and even offensive strikes against the Japanese. But these were sorely limited in scope and even more ineffectual in results, for wherever the Allies tried to hit with any sustained momentum, the Zeros quickly set things straight.

The first decisive results in stemming the Japanese tide would have to come through the United States Navy. In events seemingly unrelated, but inextricably linked with the future direct clash with units of the American fleet, the Japanese started their second wave of occupation of enemy territory.

A four-carrier force under Admiral Chuichi Nagumo, who led the attack against Pearl Harbor, arrived in late January in the south Pacific. Army and navy landing forces swept ashore at Rabaul (New Britain) and Kavieng (New Ireland). Japanese carrier planes ripped up Rabaul, Kavieng, Lae and Salamaua, the latter two targets on the northeast coast of New Guinea. What air opposition rose against the Zeros was quickly brushed aside.

By mid-February the Nagumo force, supplies replenished and ship replacements completed, struck at Port Darwin on Australia's northwest coast. Eight defending P-40s were shot out of the sky by the Zeros, and 190 Japanese planes wrought havoc in Darwin.

Heavy attacks were sustained throughout the Dutch East Indies at the same time, as Japanese land forces crushed defending Allied troops.

Everywhere the Zeros eliminated opposition from the air. Besides this, the Japanese utilized their air power to hunt down Allied warships. HMS *Prince of Wales* and HMS *Repulse* had been sunk a few days after the opening shots of war on 10th December, and Japanese ships and planes now raged through the Dutch East Indies against American, British and Dutch warships. Then, immediately preceding the scheduled strikes against Colombo in Ceylon, a reconnaissance plane caught sight of British warships in the area. The Japanese pressed home their strike on Colombo with more than 130 fighters and bombers.

The British had sighted the Japanese fleet well ahead of time, for, as Masatake Okumiya related: 'a swarm of enemy fighter planes plunged from the sky against our air formations. Again the inferior performance of the Allied fighter aircraft and the superior skill of our fighter pilots paid handsome dividends. The ensuing air battle between the approximately sixty enemy planes and our Zero fighters resulted in the destruction of almost all the enemy aircraft, which the Zeros prevented from disrupting the bomber formations.'

Immediately afterward, in a new strike, aircraft of the Nagumo force destroyed two British destroyers at sea. Or so they thought. Photos of the battle showed the warships to be the cruisers HMS *Cornwall* and HMS *Dorsetshire*. Again the Japanese moved out to strike. On 9th April a force of 125 planes smashed at Trincomalee and a huge air battle developed. Fifty-six defending fighters, including ten Hurricanes, went down (British records indicate nine out of eleven Hurricanes shot down by Zeros that day). Even more important to the Japanese was the defensive quality of the Zero. Nine Blenheim bombers attacked the Nagumo carriers and Zeros shot down every raider. Reconnaissance planes, in the meantime, had discovered the aircraft carrier HMS *Hermes* with the destroyer HMAS *Vampire*.

In what the Japanese considered the most accurate bombing they ever accomplished during the war, the *Hermes* within ten minutes was a gutted, flaming hull, on its way to

the bottom. The *Vampire* was already gone.

The Japanese now turned to executing their plans for capturing Port Moresby on the south coast of New Guinea. This was the only air base in the south-west Pacific, states Okumiya, 'from which enemy planes continued to strike back at our still-advancing forces.' If they captured Moresby, the Japanese would eliminate the danger to Rabaul and Kavieng. Simultaneously, the Japanese planned to take Tulagi in the southern Solomons, from where they would hit at New Caledonia and Fiji. By early May the Japanese had realized some of their objectives and were pushing on to complete their thrusts. But there appeared to be unexpected opposition in the form of an American task force, with at least one carrier.

The first clash between Japanese and American carriers was now imminent. Soon the Japanese would learn that two carriers were involved.

The battle was joined in a way the Japanese never expected. The *Shoho* had sent most of her Zeros to cover a transport convoy when an estimated ninety-five aircraft from the American carriers struck a devastating blow: 'Heavy bombs and torpedoes split the vessel,' Okumiya related, 'and the *Shoho* soon went down. She was the first Japanese carrier to be lost in the war.'

Japanese dive and torpedo bombers, meanwhile, had run headlong into Grumman F4F Wildcat fighters defending their own carriers. 'In the brief but sharply fought battle,' said Okumiya, 'the Grummans shot down eight of the fifteen torpedo

Without an escort of Zeros, this Kate would never have come so close to its target

bombers, and also destroyed one dive bomber.' He added that the Japanese 'fled from the hornet's nest into which they had flown'.

There was also a personal, or rather an emotional, factor to be considered as the pawns of the Battle of the Coral Sea continued their movements. The *Shoho* was the first Japanese carrier lost in the war and, Okumiya points out, 'we had failed to inflict retaliation upon the enemy carriers. To the naval personnel involved, the destruction of the *Shoho* and the subsequent inability of the Japanese planes to attack the American carriers involved great loss of pride. Aboard the *Shokaku* and the *Zuikaku*,

Admiral Hara's men grimly attended to their bombers and fighters, preparing them for combat on the following day. To "save face", they must by any means destroy the American carriers.'

On the morning of 8th May, the Japanese tore at the American fleet. *Lexington* (by US reckoning) took two torpedoes and two bombs, and *Yorktown* took one direct bomb hit. Half the entire attacking force was shot out of the air. In the meantime, *Shokaku* took three direct hits across her flight deck, putting the carrier out of the fight.

Okumiya provides the appraisal of the first fight in which the Japanese were stopped:

'Thus ended the first naval battle which was fought entirely by the air elements of the two opponents. In this initial carrier-versus-carrier

The effectiveness of Japanese tactics amply proved – wrecked US aircraft litter the deck of their carrier after being hit by a Japanese raid

contest, our carrier forces and those of the enemy were approximately equal in strength.

In the two days of fighting our carriers lost thirty-two planes either shot down or missing, and twelve additional aircraft which made forced landings. Our losses mounted when the *Zuikaku's* captain ordered several planes jettisoned overboard to clear the decks for emergency landings of the *Shokaku's* aircraft, when that carrier's own decks became entangled with wreckage. Immediately after the battle there remained on the *Zuikaku* as operational aircraft only twenty-four Zero fighters, nine Type 99 Val dive bombers, and six Type 97 Kate attack torpedo bombers. This number represented barely one-fourth of the original total of bombers aboard both carriers prior to the air battles.

These losses indicated clearly the high cost of all-out carrier warfare and for the first time enabled us to predict the outcome of future fleet engagements in which surface vessels, despite their number or power, would

play merely auxiliary roles. Over separation distances of two hundred to three hundred miles between fleets, the cruisers and battleships could contribute to the battle only by employing their anti-aircraft weapons to help defend their carriers against attacking enemy planes. In the two full days of the Coral Sea Battle, the approximate total of ninety-five vessels of both contestants, twenty-five American and seventy Japanese, did not exchange a single shot.'

What Okumiya has to say next is crucial to this book, which is primarily a study of the Zero fighter and its role in the war. A preface is necessary. The American fighters used in this engagement, and in the Battle of Midway which was to take place the following month, were primarily Grumman F4F Wildcats (there were some Brewster F2A Buffalos at Midway), a carrier-based fighter the Japanese considered basically inferior to the Zero.

Yet, in the Battle of the Coral Sea, the Zeros could not protect their own carriers. This was the significant lesson of the Coral Sea conflict, and it was to have a profound influence on the entire war, for at Midway, barely a month later, American airpower broke the back of the Japanese fleet and altered the course of the war drastically.

Masatake Okumiya continues the story:

'The Coral Sea episode also taught us to study closely the use of fighter planes in air-sea engagements. We discovered that in a long-range conflict between aircraft carriers qualitative superiority in fighter planes was not enough to stop a determined attack by enemy bombers and fighters. Quantity also was a requisite for successful defense and, even under the best possible conditions, an attack fiercely pressed home by the enemy would result in severe air losses to both sides.'

As a result of battle damage, the US Navy recorded the loss of the Lexington and minor damage to the Yorktown. The Japanese, to their everlasting regret, permitted the carrier to escape – and it later came back to haunt them. The Japanese at first considered the Coral Sea to be a victory for their side. Tactically they were correct. It took them some time to understand that, in the strategic sense, it was a defeat of monstrous implication.

What the Japanese could not realize was that the US Navy had accomplished its primary, strategic purpose. First, the Japanese called off the invasion of Port Moresby, which was to become a bastion of tremendous striking power for Allied land-based air forces.

And secondly, as Okumiya states with brutal candor:

'None of our surviving officers of the Coral Sea Battle could have forseen the terrible strategic implications of their colossal blunder. The crippled Yorktown was permitted to escape when perhaps a single torpedo or only a few bombs could have ensured that vessel's destruction. A month later, that same ship which we then permitted to survive became one of the strongest factors contributing to our navy's shattering defeat in the Battle of Midway.

Every last officer and crewman lost in the attacks on the evening of 7th May was a skilled, irreplaceable veteran. Had these men and their planes not been lost in the debacle of 7th May, they could have participated in the attack against the enemy carriers on 8th May, and, quite possibly, could have crippled the Yorktown as our remaining planes had disabled the Lexington.

In retrospect, it is no exaggeration to state that those few Grumman Wildcats which were in the air on 7th May and which intercepted our planes on their return to their own carriers saved not only the Yorktown but also eventually many other American ships then in the Coral Sea.'

And of course they also saved many US ships which might otherwise have been sunk during the Battle of Midway.

That epic struggle has been documented so extensively it needs little mention here. In regard to the Zero fighter, Midway must easily be the greatest peak of frustration ever known by fighter pilots. For the Zero was as effective at Midway as the Japanese had hoped.

During the initial Japanese strike

against Midway Island's facilities, thirty-six Zeros escorted seventy-two dive and torpedo bombers. About thirty-five miles from Midway Island twenty-seven American fighters, twenty Brewster F2A Buffalos and seven Grumman F4F Wildcats, slammed into the Japanese formations.

The Zeros were too swift and effective for the American fighters to do more than annoy the Japanese. Of the twenty-seven American fighters at least seventeen were quickly shot out of the sky (these are admitted US losses), seven more were damaged severely, and most of the surviving pilots were wounded.

In the defense of their own carrier forces the Zeros flew beautifully and fought with savage fury They were, in co-ordination with the anti-aircraft defenses of the task force, extraordinarily effective in holding off and shattering the American air attacks.

Until a final few and fateful moments when six Grumman TBF Avenger torpedo bombers, in their baptism of fire, rushed at the Japanese carriers. Five were shot down.

Four Martin B-26 Marauders went in fast and low. Zeros and flak blew two of them out of the air.

Twenty-eight Marine dive bombers, Vought SB2U Vindicators and Douglas SBD Dauntlesses, attacked fiercely. Twelve went down in flames. In the first attacking waves the Americans lost nineteen planes and crews without even scratching a Japanese warship. Seventeen Marine fighters were blown out of the air by Zeros, who lost only one of their number.

The attacks continued and the slaughter spread. Fifteen Douglas TBD Devastators of Torpedo Squadron 8 from USS *Hornet* went in low and slow. The Japanese blew every bomber out of the sky without themselves sustaining one hit. Another twenty-six torpedo bombers went in. Japanese fighters and flak shattered the attack. Twenty out of the twenty-six

bombers smashed into the water, again without inflicting any damage on the Japanese

But the stage was set. Every gun in the Japanese fleet was fully depressed to hit the torpedo bombers. The Zeros were on the deck, slashing and cutting up the torpedo bombers.

But the sky overhead was undefended. No one thought to look up. The shrill scream from the sky was heard only when it was too late.

The Dauntless dive bombers from USS *Enterprise* and USS *Yorktown* came down in near-vertical dives from 17,000 feet. For three miles they plunged at the carriers naked and exposed below them.

Soryu took three 1,000-pounds in her vitals; *Akagi* reeled from two bombs that went deep before exploding; and *Kaga* took four big bombs deep in her belly and vomited huge sheets of flame.

Within minutes all three carriers were finished.

Left: Douglas Dauntless dive bombers peel off for their attack on the Japanese carriers at the Battle of Midway. *Above:* Grumman Avengers distracted Japanese attention from the dive bombers

The next day another carrier took a series of direct hits. Midway marked the loss of four of Japan's biggest and most powerful aircraft carriers. With them went 234 aircraft and more than 2,500 men.

Within their ranks were the finest pilots and aircrews of the Imperial Japanese Navy, men who could not be replaced in time for later battles.

There were many great battles in the months to come. But as far as the United States was concerned, the final issue from that moment on was never in doubt.

The Zero, a great fighter, still the best fighter across the length of the Pacific, was not good enough any longer.

Slugging match

During the late spring and early summer of 1942 the only major Japanese air action against the enemy came from the 25th Air Flotilla, consisting of the Tainan Air Corps, the 4th Air Corps and the Yokohama Air Corps. Headquarters for these forces was Rabaul. The flotilla engaged in constant air attack, concentrating the full force of its strength against the enemy at Port Moresby in New Guinea. Of lesser consequence were the intermittent attacks which it mounted against Port Darwin with medium attack bombers of the 25th Air Flotilla, based on Timor Island. Characteristic of this phase of the war, the air attacks against the Moresby complex of shipping, base facilities and scattered airstrips were always made with comparatively heavy formations composed of twenty-seven or more medium bombers and an approximately equal number of Zero fighters. To support the ultimate plan for taking Port Moresby the Japanese on 21st July 1942 attacked Buna, on the north-eastern coast of New Guinea. The Allied reaction was violent, and the Japanese forces were subjected to

a fierce and sustained attack pressed home with suicidal courage. Determined to eliminate this unexpected heavy resistance, the Japanese planned to smash at Moresby's airfields, as well as those at Rabi, on the south-eastern end of New Guinea.

The preparations for this offensive were well under way when the Japanese were electrified with the news that American forces had landed on Guadalcanal in the southern group of the Solomon Islands. This was the first thrust back at the Japanese, the first time the Americans had attempted a combined air, land and sea assault to start the long road back.

The air battles waged from the Japanese-occupied fields of Lae and Salamaua in New Guinea, and then the intensely violent struggles in the Guadalcanal area, formed a period referred to by many veterans of those fights as an 'all-out slugging match'. In its earliest phases the Zero pilots operating. from Lae and Salamaua made up what was unquestionably the toughest fighter opposition Allied pilots knew throughout the

war in the Pacific. At these advanced Japanese fields were the greatest aces of the Imperial Navy, and they were flying fighters still considerably superior to the P-39s and the P-40s the Americans and Australians were flying from Moresby and Rabi fields. The Zeros also fought against B-17, B-25 and B-26 bombers, and against the last, twin-engined medium bombers caused some of the Pacific War's worst losses to the Americans. These battles show the Japanese pilots at their best, at the peak of their performance, and enjoying great superiority in the quality of their fighter aircraft. It was a period much too long for the Americans and all too short for the Japanese. But the long summer of repeated victories for the Japanese was nearing its end, and with the final months of 1942 the tenor of the war had changed.

Those were the months when new wings appeared in the Pacific skies, and the Japanese for the first time faced the Lockheed P-38 Lightning and the Vought F4U Corsair, fighters that were as superior in many respects to the Zero as that fighter was to the

A navy plane's gun camera records a fatal strike

Bell P-39 Airacobra. Hard on the heels of the Lightnings and Corsairs were more fighters – the Republic P-47 Thunderbolt, the Grumman F6F Hellcat and the North American P-51 Mustang. The war had changed also in other ways. When the Americans suffered losses they could replace the downed fighters with new machines. Even with the older P-39s, P-40s and F4Fs the Americans were gaining successes. Now they knew the Zero and knew how to fight the machine. The Zero remained the superior fighter, but skill and tactics on the part of the Americans were already having a grim effect on the Japanese.

But in the fighter combats which followed the Zero pilots of Lae and Salamaua reigned supreme. This was their moment, brief, to be sure, but indisputedly theirs.

With the aid of the great Japanese ace Saburo Sakai we turn back the clock to the spring of 1942:

'Early in April, thirty of us from the Tainan Wing transferred to a new air

127

The cream of Japan's fighter pilots – members of the Lae wing pose for the camera (Sakai is standing, on the left)

base at Lae, on the eastern coast of New Guinea. Captain Masashisa Saito led our group to the new installation. Then began some of the fiercest air battles of the entire Pacific war. Only 180 miles away from the Allied bastion of Port Moresby, we began our new assignments by flying escort almost daily for our bombers, which flew from Rabaul to hammer the enemy installations in the critical Moresby area. No longer was the war entirely one-sided. As often as we lashed out at Moresby, Allied fighters and bombers came to attack Lae. The valor of the Allied pilots and their willingness to fight surprised us all. Whenever they attacked Lae, they were invariably intercepted and several of their planes were damaged or shot down. Our attacks on Moresby also contributed to the Allied losses.

The willingness of the Allied pilots to engage us in combat deserves special mention here, for, regardless of the odds, their fighters were always screaming in to attack. And it is important to point out that their fighter planes were clearly inferior in performance to our own Zeros. Furthermore, almost all of our pilots were skilled air veterans; coupled with the Zero's outstanding performance, this afforded us a distinct advantage. The men we fought were among the bravest I have ever encountered, no less so than our own pilots who, three years later, went out willingly on missions from which there was no hope of return.'

On 11th April 1942 the Zero pilots flew a mission to the Port Moresby area.

'We passed over the airfield, this time with the sun directly behind us, cruising slowly when we finally sighted the enemy's planes, four P-39s, the first Airacobras I had ever seen. They were flying almost directly at us, some three miles off and to our left. It was impossible to tell yet whether or not we had been sighted. I jettisoned my fuel tank and poured power to my engine, my two wingmen right with me . . . Lieutenant Sasai waved his hand forward. "Go ahead. We'll cover you."

Not a move from the four Airacobras yet. We were in luck. With the blinding sun directly before them,

the American pilots failed to pick out our approaching fighters. The P-39s flew in two pairs, the first two planes preceding the others by about 300 yards.

I moved Honda behind and above me, and signalled the less experienced Yonekawa to follow directly behind my fighter. Then we were only 500 yards from the enemy planes, heeling over to the left. In a few seconds we would be ready to strike. If only they continued to be blinded by the sun, we could hit them before they even knew we were in the air.

Even as I was ready to roll over for the attack, I changed my approach. If I pulled up to come in from a dive, I would lose the advantage of the sun behind me. Instead, I shoved the stick forward and dove, Honda and Yonekawa sticking to me like glue. We went down and then came around in a sharp, fast turn, in perfect position.

The last two fighters were now above and ahead of me, unaware of our approach. They were still blinded, and I closed the distance steadily, waiting until it would be impossible to miss the target. The two P-39s were almost wing to wing, and at fifty yards they were clear in my range finder. *Now!* I jammed down on the cannon button, and in a second the first Airacobra was done for. The shells converged in the center of the fuselage – pieces of metal broke off and flipped away. A fountain of smoke and flame belched outward.

I skidded and brought the guns to bear on the second P-39. Again the shells went directly home, exploding inside and tearing the fighter into bits. Both Airacobras plummeted out of control.

I brought the Zero out of its skid and swung up in a tight turn, prepared to come out directly behind the two leading fighters. The battle was already over! Both P-39s were plunging crazily toward the earth, trailing bright flames and thick smoke. They had been shot down as quickly as the two I had caught so unawares. I recognized one of the Zeros still pulling out from its diving pass, Hiroyoshi Nishizawa, a rookie pilot, at the controls. The second Zero, which had made a kill with a single firing pass, piloted by Toshio Ota,

Above and below: Completely outclassed by the Zero, the Bell P-39 Airacobra's saving grace was its extraordinary strength, demonstrated in this photograph of a belly-landing

hauled around in a steep pullout to rejoin the formation.'

The rookie pilot in the Zero, Nishizawa, went on to become Japan's greatest ace of the war, with over 100 kills, before he himself was killed by Hellcat fighters – while at the controls of a troop transport!

The date is now 17th April; Sakai and his fellow pilots have just completed the escort phase of a mission:

'We passed Moresby and the bursting flak fell behind. I sighed with relief. Too soon! Nearly a mile above us, a single P-40 fighter dove with incredible speed. He came down so fast I could not move a muscle; one second he was above us, the next the lone plane plummeted like lightning into the bombers. Six hundred yards in front of me, I watched the fighter – he was going to ram!

How that plane ever got through the few yards clearance between the third and fourth bombers of the left echelon, I shall never know. It seemed impossible, but it happened. With all guns blazing, the P-40 ripped through the bomber formation and poured a river of lead into Miyazaki's plane.

Instantly the Zero burst into flames. With tremendous speed the P-40 disappeared far below us. Miyazaki's plane drifted slowly down, trailing flame. Brilliant fire flared out and an explosion tore the Zero into tiny pieces of wreckage. We failed to see even a piece of metal falling. Everything had happened in three or four seconds.'

Sakai and his fellow pilots at Lae built up their scores to become, at the time, the highest ranking aces of all Japan's air combat units. They were the pick of Japan, the best the Emperor could produce. But not even the best always perform well, as Sakai shows us in this incident that took place two days after Miyazaki was shot down and killed:

'Seven B-26 bombers attacked Lae. Fortunately, we received sufficient advance warning and had nine fighters in the air to meet the planes as they stormed in at a height of only 1,500 feet. For an hour we fought a bitter running battle with the Marauders; in the end only one bomber went down, with another fleeing as a cripple. It was the clumsiest air fight I had ever seen. The nine Zeros lacked organization. Instead of making concerted attacks against one or two planes, and using massed firepower to cut the B-26s apart, our pilots were overzealous and threw themselves all over the sky. Repeatedly several planes jerked frantically out of their firing passes to avoid a collision with another Zero or to evade the fire of a friendly fighter. It was incredible that none of our planes rammed into another or shot any of us down.'

Like fighter pilots anywhere the aces of Lae sometimes went through a 'slump period' when they could not do anything right. Saburo Sakai describes his elation at breaking out of a bad stretch of a half-dozen battles in which he failed to score any kills. And then:

'I broke out of my slump – as did Nishizawa – the day after the strafing attack by the P-39s. Nine of us flew to Moresby, spoiling for a fight. We got one. Nine enemy fighters, P-39s and P-40s, waited for us over the enemy airstrip, willing to fight.

Hardly were we in sight when they broke off their circle and roared head-on against our planes. I took on the first enemy fighter. The P-40 rolled into a turn as he came at me, hoping for a belly shot. I cut sharply inside him and fired. I could not have timed it better; the P-40 staggered into the burst. Instantly the enemy pilot snapped over in a left roll, but he was already too late. Another burst and the fighter exploded in flames.

But he had friends and I jerked out of my turn as a P-39 dove on me. No need to run for it; I drew a split-S and the enemy pilot walked right into the trap. For a moment his belly hung before my guns as he tried to loop away. I needed only that moment and I squeezed the cannon trigger. The shells caught enemy fighter while it was still pulling up, and the plane fell apart in the air.

He was sure, I knew, to have a wingman, and even as I fired my burst I had the stick hard back and the rudder bar all the way down, horsing the Zero back into the tightest turn I could make. It worked; I came out in line

Hiroyishi Nishizawa, greatest Japanese ace, with 102 kills

for a quick burst. The startled pilot tried to disengage by diving, but too late. I rolled out of the turn in time to snap out another burst. The enemy fighter flew directly into my fire, staggered, then plunged in a dive.'

The following incident, bizarre as it may seem to the reader, actually happened. The writer checked this material with the greatest of care, and talked to several Americans who were at Moresby at the time. They corroborated in full the details just as Saburo Sakai told them to the writer:

'Several Zeros broke from the battle to shoot up the field, which proved later to be their undoing. Two fighters, badly shot up, crashed on the Owen Stanley slopes during the return trip.

After the dogfight we reformed. As soon as we were in formation I signalled to Commander Nakajima that I was going down in pursuit of an enemy plane; he waved his hand and I dropped down in a long turning dive.

I was back at Moresby in a few minutes, circling above the field at 12,000 feet. The anti-aircraft remained quiet, and no enemy fighters appeared. Then two Zeros came in at my height, and we fell into formation. Nishizawa and Ota grinned at me and I waved back in greeting.

We gathered in a formation with only a few scant feet between our wing tips. I slid my canopy back, described a ring over my head with my finger, then showed them three fingers. Both pilots raised their hands in acknowledgement. We were to fly three loops, all tied together.

One last look for enemy fighters, and I nosed down to gain speed, Nishizawa and Ota hugging my own plane. I pulled back on the stick and the Zero responded beautifully in a high arcing climb, rolling over on her back. The other two fighters were right with me, all the way up and around in a perfect inside loop.

Twice more we went up and around, dove, and went back into the loop. Not a single gun fired from the ground, and the air remained clear of any enemy planes.

When I came out of the third loop

One less to contend with as a Zero goes down with flames pouring from its belly

Nishizawa pulled up to my plane, grinning happily, and signalled that he wanted to do it again. I turned to my left; there was Ota, laughing, nodding his head in agreement. I couldn't resist the temptation. We dove to only 6,000 feet above the enemy field and repeated the three loops, swinging around in perfect formation. And still not a gun fired at us! We might have been over our own field for all the excitement we seemed to create. But I thought of all the men on the ground watching us and I laughed loudly.

We returned to Lae twenty minutes after the other fighters landed. We told no one of what we had done. As soon as we could get together by ourselves, we broke into loud laughter and whoops. Ota howled with glee, and even the stoic Nishizawa slapped our backs with enjoyment. Our secret, however, was not to remain ours very long. Just after nine o'clock that night an orderly approached us in the billet and stated that Lieutenant Sasai wished to see us — immediately.

We looked at each other, not a little worried. We could receive serious punishment for what we had done.

No sooner did we walk into Sasai's office than the lieutenant was on his feet, shouting at us. "Look here, you silly bastards!" he roared, "just look at this!" His face was red and he could hardly control himself as he waved a letter - in English - before our faces. "Do you know where I got this thing?" he yelled. "No? I'll tell you, you fools; it was dropped on this base a few minutes ago by an enemy intruder!"

The letter read: "To the Lae Commander: We were much impressed with those three pilots who visited us today, and we all liked the loops they flew over our field. It was quite an exhibition. We would appreciate it if these same pilots returned here once again, each wearing a green muffler around his neck. We're sorry we couldn't give them better attention on their last trip, but we will see to it that the next time they will receive an all-out welcome from us."

It was all we could do to keep from bursting out with laughter. The letter was signed by a group of fighter pilots at Moresby. Lieutenant Sasai

kept us at ramrod attention and lectured us severely on our "idiotic behavior". We were ordered specifically never to stage any more flying exhibitions over enemy fields.'

We have the rare opportunity to compare in detail the diaries of the Japanese pilots, especially Saburo Sakai, against the records kept by the bomber crews who flew against the aces at Lae and at Salamaua, and sometimes against Rabaul. These were the men of the 22nd Bomb Group, flying Martin B-26 Marauders. Lieutenant Louis W Ford, for example, admits readily that during early 1942 the Japanese 'enjoyed a solid air superiority over New Guinea . . . I hate to be specific, of course, but it's completely accurate to say that our average losses approximated between fifteen and twenty-five per cent per mission.'

Captain John N Ewbank, Jr (today a Brigadier-General, USAF) said it

without any mincing of words:

'Who was the nut who told everybody back in the States that the Japanese were no match for us in the air? Those Japanese we met over New Guinea and up at Rabaul weren't just good – they were hell on wheels. They were real good. We never had a doubt in the world that we were slugging it out with the cream of the crop. And Lae was about the worst of all. You were raked over the hot coals just about every single time you made that haul over the mountains . . . It was rugged, real rugged. Those Japanese were some damned fine flying people, let me tell you.'

Saburo Sakai recalls a strike against Lae by seven B-26 bombers which came in low over the jungle. 'We failed to see the bombers before they were over the field, their black bombs tumbling through the air to send geysers of flame and dirt high above the runway. Even as we wheeled

in pursuit several fighters shot into the air from the field, and more than twenty-six Zeros in all went racing madly after the seven fleeing B-26s. For several moments there was near chaos in the sky as everyone rolled madly to get away from the other pursuing planes. Collisions were averted by only a few feet.'

Then, we have the words of Captain John N Ewbank, Jr, who also was there that day:

'The mission called for us to make the flight to the target right on top of a cloud deck, and then to break through and go busting over Lae. Hit them with complete surprise.'

I led that mission. Everything was going fine; we thought we really had it made. But all of a sudden we had company.

This was the first mission I had ever made when the Zeros ringed me in. I thought we had full surprise, and the funny thing is, we did. But

The Zero's opposition in New Guinea, the versatile, fast and well-armed Martin B-26 Marauder, inflicted great losses but did not remain unscathed

the moment we were in sight we could see activity ahead of us. We were really moving, too. By the time we got to the end of the runway I was staring at those Zeros scrambling into the air like a swarm of gnats. They just hauled those planes right up at us, and then came running for us straight out of their takeoff runs. I'd never seen anything like it.

We went low over the field, bombs cascading down from us, and our gunners not knowing whether to shoot up the targets on the ground, on the field, or to try to track those Zeros that were clawing at us. Soon as we got the bombs out, I turned sharply and led the formation down low over the water. But the Zero pilots acted like they were pretty mad because they hadn't been able to stop the attack. When we turned to head for home they cut inside real tight and fast and then they were all over us. They stayed with us and gave us hell. They was also the first time I brought my aircraft home a flying wreck, we were so full of gashes and holes. They really gave us a going-over. They came in to pointblank range as though our gunners weren't even there, and then they hosed everything they had at us. And they had plenty.'

Jerry Crosson of the 22nd tells how they knew when they were in there against the professionals.

'There was this one particular Zero that spelled trouble. I had watched him lead the attack into Krell's flight, and he flew – that pilot in that Japanese fighter – as if we didn't have a gun that could bother him. We were moving off to the right from the northeast coast of New Guinea when again I saw that particular Zero boring in . . .

He kept coming in from three o'clock out of a shallow diving attack, a shallow diving turn. He stayed in this turn, really coming in fast, and suddenly he screamed over us with murderous speed. I'd guess he was maybe a hundred feet or so right over us, no more than that, but perspectives are rough to judge under those conditions. He was a pro; he wasn't wasting any ammunition in that long curve, and he was just a hairsbreadth away from a skid; not skidding, but squeezing all the performance out of that aircraft. A real master; he waited for just the right moment. You can spot the master at this sort of thing right away. A lot of the rookies would splash their ammo all over the sky, but the pros who'd been around for a while knew just what they were doing. And then in a blue he was gone.

My top turret gunner – Johnston – had been tracking this same Zero, and he called on the intercom that the Zero had suddenly flashed up and down . . . twisting like a dervish so that he couldn't track him with his guns.'

And then came 7th August 1942 and the invasion of Guadalcanal, and the story of one of many units that fought there. This unit is the 67th Fighter Squadron of the Army Air Force, who had the unhappy task of flying the Bell P-400 Airacobra, the export version of the P-39, as well as an odd batch of regular P-39 fighters. Many of the pilots in the 67th had flown combat with this aircraft in the New Guinea area. Indeed, one of the combat veterans (from the 8th Fighter Group) from the New Guinea fighting was Buzz Wagner, who with the P-40 made himself the first American ace of the war. The P-39 and its export version, as described by Wagner in an official report shortly before the Guadalcanal battle, was hardly the kind of plane to endear itself to a pilot. Wagner's report stated that:

'There has seldom been an even fight between Japanese Zero type fighters and our own. Only by virtue of armor plate protection, leak-proof fuel tanks, and ruggedness of construction of our fighters, have there not been a great many more of our pilots killed and aircraft destroyed. Our fighter pilots have proven their courage and ability to fight continuously against superior odds and still maintain a very high morale. This high morale, however, has been with fighter pilots a forced one, with the knowledge that Japanese fighter would be just as high above tomorrow as they were today, and that the first enemy combat would be an attack from above out of the sun.'

Some excerpts from the history of the 67th Squadron speak with such eloquence they need no further comment:

'Then the wingman discovered tracers passing his cockpit and a Zero on his tail. He had heard that "the Zero is so flimsily constructed, its wings will come off in a dive", so he puts his P-400 in a dive, making right aileron rolls on the way down. When he pulled out he looked back to see the pieces of the Zero floating down, but found that the Zero, defying all the intelligence reports to date, was still intact, and furthermore was on his tail, shooting. It was another one of those things the 67th learned the hard way. He screamed over his radio for help .' And also this item: 'The Zeros dived down around a cloud and then zoomed up into the six P-400s from behind and below. There were

about twenty of them . . . The P-400s
started turning into a Lufberry [a defensive circle] but there were more
Zeros in the Lufberry than there
were P-400s. Then the Grumman
Wildcats came down from above
and hit the Zeros. The mixup began.
Zeros were everywhere, zipping, darting and twisting, climbing straight
up, and practically making square
turns. The 67th pilots, in their heavy,
lumbering P-400s, felt like a herd
of cows being attacked on every flank
by agile wolves.

It was impossible to shake the Zeros
by trying to maneuver. The only way
was to head down into a cloud, make a
turn on instruments, and come out
on top. Then try to get a burst at a
Zero before three others jumped you.
All over the sky P-400s were running
for the clouds with two or three Zeros
on their tails . . .

. . . We can't climb high enough to
reach the bombers. We have already
lost two pilots and half our planes
proving what we already knew – that
we can't maneuver and dogfight with

**Beginning at last to be outclassed,
from the middle of 1943 few
Zeros could return from combat
without any damage**

the Zero. What good are we? Hell, we
can't fight . . .

. . . the 67th was willing. It wanted
to fight. *But how?'*

The 67th fought – by being taken out
of air combat missions and assigned
to attacking the Japanese by strafing
and bombing. They did a remarkably
good job, too. But there was always
the reminder that they could not
fight the enemy in the air, and that
the Marines could and did.

But although neither they nor the
Japanese were aware of it, the end was
in sight for the Zero.

Defeat would come in many ways to
the Japanese.

But they would know its name best
in the form of the Lightning, Corsair,
Hellcat, Thunderbolt and Mustang.

The new American fighters, every
one of them superior to the Zero
fighter, were on their way.

Final act

The Japanese started their air war with the most outstanding fighter used anywhere across Asia and the Pacific. After several years of war more than half of all Japan's fighters were still the same basic aircraft, the Mitsubishi Type 0 fighter.

The United States discovered that its fighters were woefully inadequate to meet the Zero on even terms. The Brewster Buffalo was virtually a suicide plane in combat with the Zero. The Curtiss Tomahawk and Kittyhawk could survive only if its pilots practised the rules of survival in the same air with the Zero. The rules were even more severe for the men who flew the Bell P-400 and P-39 models of the Airacobra. The one fighter with a halfway chance of slugging it out with the Zero was the Grumman F4F Wildcat, although if the two opposing pilots were of equal skill it was the Zero that held the distinct advantage.

The beginning of the end came late in 1942 with the big, fast, heavily-armed Lockheed P-38 Lightning. At first the Lightning pilots committed the fatal error of mixing it up with the Zero, but they learned their lessons quickly and began to make the most of the Lightning's superior speed, firepower, range, altitude ability, and ruggedness. Short and simple, as the Japanese put it, the P-38 pilots could select the moments when *they* wanted to fight; they used their advantages to the utmost, and the Zero pilots suddenly found themselves on the short end of the stick.

The kill ratio enjoyed by the Zeros went through a violent reversal. Now it was the American pilots who came home with their number intact, and with claims of a half-dozen or more kills at the expense of their enemy.

Soon after the appearance of the Lightnings, the US Marines and Navy started to operate the newest powerhouse in the sky, the Chance-Vought F4U Corsair, a monster with 2,000 horsepower in the nose, an inverted gull wing, and nothing but trouble from nose to tail for the Zeros. Fast, heavily-armed and rugged, the Corsairs ran amuck among the enemy. Again the kill ratio in favour of the Japanese dropped drastically.

As fast as it was possible to do so,

Above: A Lockheed Lightning on the tail of a Zero. *Below and bottom:* The new breed of American fighters – the P-38 Lightning and the Vought Corsair

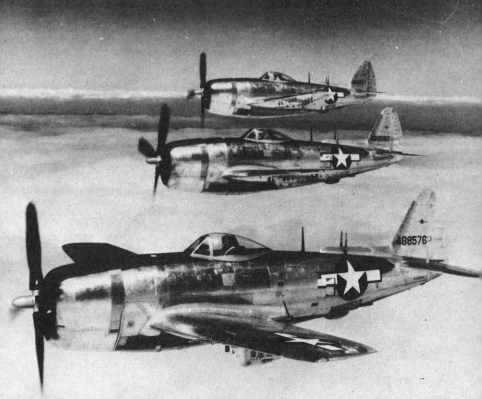

Left above: Superior in performance and also capable of turning with the Zero — the Grumman F6F Hellcat. *Left below:* Immensely strong and fast, the P-47 Thunderbolt was more than a match for the Zero. *Above:* Superior even in range to the Zero, the P-51 could easily dictate the terms on which it would fight a Zero

the United States heaped its Brewster Buffalo fighters on the junk pile. The P-39s, P-40s and F4Fs, the moment it was possible in terms of replacements, were reassigned to missions that kept them out of slugging matches with the Zero. Then in 1943 the US Navy introduced into the Pacific the one fighter that could take on the Zero under any conditions – the Grumman F6F Hellcat. Like the Corsair, the Hellcat had an engine of 2,000 horsepower. It carried six .50 caliber machine guns and an ammunition load twice as great as its forerunners. It could outclimb the Zero, it could dive faster than its enemy, it carried heavy armor plating and self-sealing fuel tanks and its construction was rugged and, most important of all, it could get into a tight turn with the Zero and stay in thoro, the pilot pulling back on the stick and matching the tightness of turns or loops of his adversary.

Republic's big P-47 Thunderbolt did not make the Japanese any happier. The famed 'Jug' could not turn with a Zero, but like the Corsair it could do everything else and do it with lethal effectiveness.

North American's P-51 Mustang came along much later in the war, and by the time it showed up the back of Japanese air-power had already been broken. The other fighters were bad enough but the Mustang capped the troubles of the Japanese pilots. Among other things it was 100 mph faster than the Zero, which gave the Mustang pilots a pleasant feeling of advantage. Of course, there were other Japanese fighters, but their number was too few and they were scattered too thinly to make any difference.

Even during the last phases of the war more than half of all the Japanese fighters in operational service were still Zeros.

Time had caught up with the pride of Mitsubishi.

The Japanese were well aware that they must, firstly, improve the qualities of the Zero, and, secondly, replace it with a better fighter as quickly as they could do so. They accomplished the first goal through constant modifications to the machine, but these fell far behind the great performance leaps of the new American fighters.

The Zero 32, which featured clipped wingtips and was introduced to combat in 1942, went through further modifications when operational use proved that performance losses outweighed the gain. Accordingly, the Japanese modified the airplane again by replacing the full wingspan, re-installing folding wingtips, and adding additional fuel tanks within the wings to increase the range. Thus the A6M3 Model 32 was the first into combat (code name 'Hamp') and was followed by the A6M3 Model 22. Exclusive of other companies' production, Mitsubishi built 343 Zero 32 and 560 Zero 22 fighters.

Another navy requirement, for a two-seat variant of the Zero to be used as a trainer, cut down on the number of Zero fighters that could be rushed to the combat zones. Early in 1942 engineers modified the A6M2 Model 21 for this purpose; the new trainer was designated 17-*Shi* Fighter Trainer. An enlarged cockpit was built for instructor and student, although the sliding canopy covered only the instructor's position and left the student out in the open in the front cockpit. For added stability small horizontal fins were mounted on the rear fuselage. To meet the needs of gunnery training two 7.7-mm machine guns were mounted. It entered production as the A6M2-K Zero-Renson in two factories other than the Mitsubishi one (Sasebo 21st Naval Air Arsenal which built 236 models, and Hitachi-Chiba, which built 272). The maximum speed of the A6M2-K was 296 mph at 12,120 feet.

'Although the Guadalcanal campaign was at its peak in land, sea, and air fighting,' explains Jiro Horikoshi, 'the long-awaited 14-*Shi* interceptor, later the J2M *Raiden* (Thunderbolt), lagged in development, and was far behind its original schedule. Since we could not count on the new aircraft's arrival at the front for many months to come, we had again to turn to improving the Zero fighter's performance in order to contest the new American fighters which in many respects now clearly out-performed the earlier Zero models.'

The new A6M5 Model 52 fighter was the most numerous of all the Zero models and was rushed into production both by Mitsubishi (which built 747) and Nakajima. The Zero 52 could best be described as a marriage of convenience between production and performance demands, as Jiro Horikoshi relates:

'Our first attempts were directed to simplifying production, and to increasing the diving speed. We reduced the wingspan again, and eliminated the wing-folding mechanism. To obtain every possible speed advantage our engineers replaced the old exhaust stacks with individual stacks which directed the exhaust gas backwards at high velocity. These changes produced a maximum level speed which for the first time exceeded 345 mph. Despite its increase of 440 lbs in weight over the Zero 32 of the same wingspan, the new Zero 52 reached 351 mph in level flight at 20,000 feet, and clearly indicated an improved rate of climb. Heavier-gauge wing skin allowed a marked increase in the diving speed limit, which now exceeded an indicated airspeed of 410 mph.'

The demands for improved performance never slackened and, when replacement designs failed to appear at the front, the navy pressed Mitsubishi to continue its design-improvement program with the Zero, for there was no other way out of the dilemma of matching combat zone demands with slowed production and introduction of wholly new fighters.

The first of the new models was the A6M5a Zero 52, the prototype of which was flying in late 1943, and for which production started in March 1944 (Mitsubishi built 391, apart from Nakajima production). 'In the A6M5a,' explains Horikoshi, 'we adopted the belt-feed system for the 20mm wing cannon, thereby increasing the ammunition supply from 100 to 125 rounds per cannon. The increase of wing

Above: Zero A6M2-K two-seat trainer. *Below:* An A6M5 Model 52, with extra thrust provided by the exhaust ejector stubs from the engine

Above: An A6M5b Model 52b, which had increased armament in the fuselage. *Right above:* Introducing a much heavier armament and increased pilot and fuel protection, the A6M5c was considerably underpowered

rigidity resulting from partial increase in the wing gauge permitted an increase in the dive-limit speed from the previous 410 mph indicated airspeed to 460 mph. This proved to be the maximum possible gain in diving speed, and the engineers did not attempt to increase the limit beyond this point. We were pleased with our engineers' efforts, for even the heavy F4U Corsair fighter then in active service was limited to a diving speed of 489 mph IAS (Indicated Air Speed).'

The A6M5b Zero 52 first flew in 1944 and Mitsubishi built 470 of this variant. This model received a slight improvement in firepower, the first since the initial prototype was built. The nose armament now comprised one 7.7mm and one 12.7mm (approximately .50 caliber) machine guns. Armor glass was installed directly behind the windshield glass for added pilot protection, and additional safety for the pilot was incorporated in the form of automatic fire extinguishers in the wing fuselage fuel tanks. Mass production started in April 1944.

The navy's 'white hope' in the new Zero series was the A6M5c Model 52c, which was intended to give the Zero the ability to slug it out with the Hellcat fighters rampaging through the Pacific, but the new model never met its predicted performance. Jiro Horikoshi explains why:

'On 23rd July 1944 the Navy issued a maximum priority order calling for (1) the installation of two 13mm wing-mounted machine guns placed outboard of the main landing gear, in addition to the 13mm gun in the fuselage and two 20mm wing cannon; (2) armor glass and steel armor plate at the rear of the pilot's seat; (3) installation of special racks beneath each wing to accommodate small rocket bombs; (4) a 31-gallon self-sealing fuel tank placed behind the cockpit, and (5) a maximum dive speed limit of 460 mph indicated airspeed to be maintained through the

use of thickened wing skin gauge. It was next to impossible for the Mitsubishi design staff, burdened as they were with other responsibilities, to accomplish all these modifications in a short period of time. They would have to add more than 660 pounds to the gross weight of the airplane as compared to the A6M5b model, causing an inevitable loss of performance. The makeshift design and workmanship resulting from the "crash" program could not help impairing the wing's exterior smoothness. If the Zero retained its original *Sakae* 21 engine, its performance would drop so sharply that despite the heavier armament, armor plating, and self-sealing fuel tanks, it would be even more at the mercy of the high-performance Hellcats. Under these circumstances, the airplane could not possibly compete with the F6F Hellcat; but, argued the Mitsubishi design staff, with the increased power of the *Kinsei* 62 engine, the Zero might well be restored to a performance equality with the American carrier fighter.

To the bewilderment of the designers the navy refused the engine change, claiming that the expected delay of several months required for adapting the new engine to the Zero was out of the question. Water-methanol injection, insisted the navy, would provide the emergency power needed. The navy erred, for they overestimated badly the power gains which reputedly could be obtained through such a modification to the *Sakae* 21 engine. Mitsubishi, however, could only follow the navy's orders.

Mitsubishi dispatched its new Zero development engineer, Eitaro Sano, to the Naval Air Research and Development Center [NARDC]. Sano and his team labored day and night with the Center's technicians to facilitate company-navy co-ordination on the new project. The team was efficient and in record-breaking time completed the modification program. Early in September 1944, about one month prior to the invasion of Leyte, the first A6M5c fighter, modified from and A6M5 airframe, was completed at the NARDC factory.

The first prototype suffered from a reduction in wing torsional rigidity, however, and, consequently, its maxi-

147

Above and below: Two views of an A6M6c, which featured the increased armament of the A6M5c but into which Horikoshi was forced to fit a *Sakae* 31 engine with water-methanol injection

mum diving speed was limited. Heavier wing skin eliminated this fault in subsequent models. The *Sakae* 31A engine with water-methanol injection failed to complete its test runs in time for the new A6M5c fighter, and the aircraft went into production without added power necessitated by its sharp weight increase. As predicted by Mitsubishi, performance fell off badly. Mitsubishi produced only ninety-three models.'

Another problem encountered with the A6M5c was that it went into production without the self-sealing tanks demanded by the navy. With little experience in this equipment the Mitsubishi engineers encountered problems that caused serious delays in production, forcing the navy to accept the machine without the fire protection it needed so badly. As the A6M5c started moving off the lines, the long-awaited *Sakae* 31 engine and the fuel tanks of self-sealing design finally became available. Mitsubishi rushed out the first Zero 53c model, the A6M6c, with hopes that the new fighter would make up the severe performance loss of its predecessor. Instead of high performance they found hair-pulling frustration. The new engine produced far less power than had been promised by Nakajima. Now they had on their hands a new fighter that not only was below the power rating of the underpowered A6M5c, but suffered repeated engine failures. 'The engine's methanol metering device failed repeatedly,' reported Horikoshi, 'and the entire powerplant became a nightmare of complicated maintenance problems to our mechanics.'

Mitsubishi produced only the one prototype, and the Zero 53c program was cancelled.

By the last months of 1944 Japan's critical position in the war demanded emergency measures from its pilots and its planes. The navy was still flying the same dive bomber, the Aichi 99, which it had been using in combat in China long before the attack on Pearl Harbor. The Aichi 99's performance was the same in late 1944 that it had been in 1940 and it was particularly vulnerable to the newer American fighters. A crash program to produce aircraft carriers meant using small, lightweight vessels; the Aichi 99 was too fast and too heavy to operate from such warships. The navy, in its search for a bomber to operate from the light carriers, found it was unable to use the newer Aichi D4Y3 *Suisei* dive bomber; the *Suisei* was even faster than the Zero in level flight, but was also too fast to operate from the new carriers.

The only aircraft available was the Zero, which as an emergency measure the navy modified to fill the need for a dive bomber. Existing Zeros were equipped with a special mechanism to carry a 550-pound bomb beneath the fuselage, but the Zero performed its new role poorly. Often the bomb-release mechanism failed, and many pilots far out at sea, near their targets, found they could not get rid of the heavy missile beneath the fighter. Consequently, still burdened with the weight and drag of the bomb, they crashed, out of fuel, as they tried to return to their home fields. For a while such losses exceeded the number of Zeros lost in the attacks.

In late 1944, when the modified Zeros went into service, the Japanese started their *Kamikaze* attacks. The Zeros sent out on such missions were the first planes used for the suicide dives, and bomb-release difficulties under such circumstances, of course, meant nothing, since the plane would never return, anyway. The bomb-carrying *Kamikaze* Zeros went to *Air Group 201* in the Philippines and became the first planes to go out on planned, deliberate suicide dives.

But not all missions were to be suicide, and the navy was still in desperate need for a reliable dive bomber to operate from its light carriers. To remedy the defects of the stopgap Zeros used for dive bombing, Mitsubishi built the A6M7 variant, the Zero 63, which went into production in May 1945 with both Mitsubishi and Nakajima (production records were destroyed and the number built is unknown). Mitsubishi reinforced the horizontal stabilizers, designed a new and reliable bomb-release mechanism, and installed racks for two underwing auxiliary fuel tanks, so that the bomb could be carried beneath the

Above and below: The final fling – a mortally-hit *kamikaze* aircraft continues ploughing toward its target but blows up just before impact

belly without appreciable loss in range.

Before turning to the last variant of the Zero, let us turn back the clock to consider a variant not mentioned before, the A6M4, which for many years has been unknown but which has recently come to light. The designation A6M4 has now been found to apply to two A6M2s experimentally fitted with a turbo-supercharged version of the *Sakae* engine by the Yokosuka First Naval Air Technical Arsenal in 1943. Development of alloys necessary for the proper running of the supercharger was very slow, however, and further development was cancelled after a series of failures and fires.

Now we come to the last major variant of the basic Zero design. For years Mitsubishi had fought a steady battle with the navy to obtain a more powerful engine for the Zero, and consistently had been met with refusals. Finally, a combination of circumstances brought to Mitsubishi what it considered to be a moral victory and renewed hopes to build a Zero with *improved* performance

over previous models. The navy agreed to use the *Kinsei* 62 engine, a 14-cylinder twin-row radial of 1,500 horsepower in a new Zero variant. The requirements for the fighter called for complete replacement of the wing fuel-tank inner sealant protection with automatic fire extinguishers; increased fuel capacity to maintain a flight time of thirty minutes under full power for combat, plus two hours and thirty minutes cruise; and the removal of the fuselage-mounted 13mm machine gun to keep aircraft weight to its minimum.

The crash program to build the new Zero, which became the A6M8c Zero 64, ran into one snag after another. Japanese industry was already suffering severely from lack of quality materials. Many of the factory workers had been drafted and their replacements were unskilled in their tasks, which resulted, as Horikoshi put it, 'in many aircraft parts of inferior manufacture'. There was also the problem of bombing by US aircraft, for B-29 raids had forced a drastic dispersal of industrial facili-

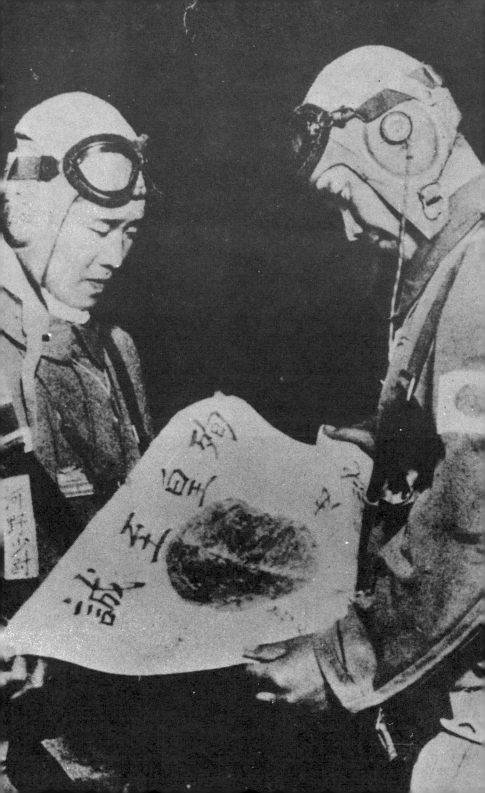

Above: Boeing B-29 Superfortresses, a hard prey for the Zero in the air, and destroyer of Zero production on the ground in the Japanese homeland *Left: Kamikaze* pilots about to leave on their one-way mission

ties. 'These same adverse conditions,' noted Horikoshi, 'extended beyond airframe manufacturing centers to include engine plants and also brought about a reduction in the quality of aviation fuel. The combinations of poorly finished aircraft surfaces, engine parts of inferior quality, and petrol of lowered octane could only mean an overall loss of performance in all new aircraft.'

Despite all the above problems, to which was added severe damage suffered in B-29 bombings, the first prototype of the new A6M8c fighter flew in late April 1945. There were many minor engineering problems and some of a major nature, but these were quickly attended to by Mitsubishi, and when the 'bugs' were removed, the Zero 64 reached a maximum level speed of 355 mph at 19,700 feet, and climbed in six minutes fifty seconds from a standing start to 19,700 feet. The fact that this was possible with a record gross weight of 6,940 pounds was a tribute to the basic design.

The Zero 64, although somewhat slower than the Hellcat, was considered by the Japanese to be equal to the powerful American fighter.

For the first time in its long history the Zero not only would go into combat with the agility its pilots had always demanded, but would do so with armor plating, armor glass, self-extinguishing fuel tanks and heavy armament.

At the Yokosuka Experimental Air Corps Proving Division at Misawa Airbase in Aomori Prefecture two Zero 64 prototypes were put through rigorous testing, earning the plaudits of the test pilots.

The navy ordered production to begin immediately. A total of 6,500 Zero 64 fighters were scheduled to be manufactured during the next twelve months.

This production was never achieved, for time had run out and the war was lost.

There were a number of other variants to the basic Zero fighter which never received official designations. Most of these modifications were made in the field at different technical and engineering centers, and reflected immediate combat requirements. To meet the threat of the B-29s, and to add the force of Zero fighters to other planes used against the giant raiders, field centers

eliminated the lightweight machine guns in the nose and increased the wing armament to a total of four 20mm cannon. Some Zeros carried a fifth 20mm cannon, mounted behind the pilot, in the rear fuselage to fire up at an angle of thirty degrees, to the left of the pilot. This design was intended to permit a Zero pilot to climb directly beneath a B-29, hold formation at very close range, and pump explosive shells into the belly of the enemy bomber.

By the war's end, despite the loss of the intended Zero 64 program, more Zero fighters had been built by Japan than any other type of aircraft. Mitsubishi in its different factories turned out 3,879 models, but the big producer was Nakajima which manufactured a total of 6,215 Zeros. To this is added the total of 844 trainers and float-plane fighters, for a grand total of 10,938 Zeros.

The epitaph for the Zero, of course, must be in the words of the man who gave it birth, Jiro Horikoshi:

'Unfortunately neither the navy nor the aviation companies understood properly the manpower requirements of aeronautical design under the stress of war. Those men charged directly with development of the Zero fighter were forced to spread their time and energy thinly, owing to unrealistic assignments to other projects even as they labored to bring about a "new" Zero. Thus we failed to achieve our original goals; the Zero lacked the improvements possible in the aircraft, and the new fighter types suffered from haphazard attention. Had the navy and the aircraft companies properly anticipated our wartime engineering needs, the A6M8c Zero 64 fighter could have appeared at the front by the spring of 1943 and certainly could have done much to hold back the enemy Hellcats which stormed over our fighters.

Our navy commanders failed also to anticipate the fast-flowing technological stream of aviation developments . . . The production and modification trail which the Zero followed was erratic and at times stumbling, notably in the war's later stages. As had happened on so many previous occasions, the fate of the Zero fighter proved an accurate reflection of the

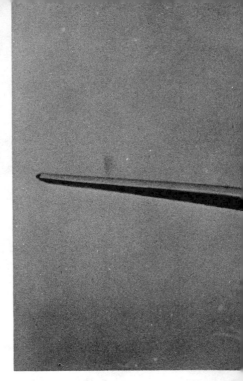

entire navy's status.

To foreign designers, notably the Americans, who always appeared to us to modify successfully their aircraft with breakneck speed, the Zero modification program appeared to move slowly and too often without regard to the lessons of the battlefront. This was by no means the case. We failed to keep pace with foreign technological developments only because Japan suffered from a second-rate industrial capacity. Our aircraft industry received support from what can be considered only as backward industry; we struggled against the drawback of few experienced engineers and poor natural resources, all of which demanded overlong time for design proposals, experiments, construction, testing and placement of new aircraft in service.

Foreign manufacturers dispatched engineering teams to the forward bases so that mechanics and aircrew members would be fully 'aware of every problem with which they might be confronted. Not only did this practice assure the best possible maintenance procedures, but it facili-

tated the collection of operational lessons which allowed the various companies promptly to modify their planes still on the production line. The system paid tremendous dividends. Our army and navy similarly followed the engineers-in-the-field program, but they were handicapped by a never-solved shortage of experienced engineers. Therefore the Japanese program achieved only a fraction of the effectiveness of the Allied system. Our engineers were capable men, but they were saddled with an antiquated industry which required excessive time in which to develop new ideas into practical equipment.

Although our industry did not meet the standards of the American aeronautical giants, even those few advantages we possessed often were wasted through sheer administrative inefficiency. Incompetent planning and leadership wasted the time of our engineers and of course, resulted in a definite reduction of aircraft coming off the production line. Sometimes our "planners" became so overwrought about engineering operational reports that their modification orders to the factories overlapped previous changes; more often, a steady flow of minor modifications swamped the scanty engineering staffs, with the result that they attended to minor matters but could not devote their time to the major issues at hand. Too many projects for developments of aircraft further dispersed the hard core of experienced engineers with the inevitable result that, while the entire industry dragged itself along, few vitally needed projects reached completion. In these circumstances, then, it is understandable that Japan so often failed to meet its original goals with new aircraft.'

But for a while, for a brief period of its air war, the Zero received the highest accolades of all, from the men who flew against it:

'Zeros were everywhere, zipping, darting and twisting, climbing straight up, and practically making square turns. The 67th pilots, in their heavy, lumbering P-400s, felt like a herd of cows being attacked on every flank by agile wolves.'

Type	Model	Engine hp	Armament	Speed/Height	Climb	Ceiling	Range
A5M4		Nakajima *Kotobuki* 41, 710 hp	2 × 7.7mm 2 × 66-lb bombs	279 mph at 10,500 feet	5 minutes 54 seconds to 16,405 ft	32,150 feet	746 miles max
A6M1		Mitsubishi MK2 *Zuisei* 13,875 hp	2 × 20 mm 2 × 7.7 mm 2 × 66-lbs or 132-lbs bombs	304 mph at 12,470 feet	5 minutes 15 seconds 16,405 feet		
A6M2	21	Nakajima NK1C *Sakae* 12, 950 hp	2 × 20 mm 2 × 7.7mm 2 × 66-lbs or 132-lbs bombs	332 mph at 16,570 feet	7 minutes 27 seconds 19,685 feet	33,790 feet	1,930 miles max
A6M2	11	Nakajima NK1C *Sakae* 12, 950 hp	2 × 20mm 2 × 7.7 mm 2 × 66-lbs or 132-lbs bombs	332 mph at 16,570 feet	7 minutes 27 seconds 19,685 feet	33,790 feet	1,930 miles max
6M2-N		Nakajima NK1C *Sakae* 12, 950 hp	2 × 20mm 2 × 7.7mm 2 × 66-lbs or 132-lbs bombs	271 mph at 16,405 feet	6 minutes 43 seconds to 16,405ft	32,810 feet	1,100 miles max
A6M3	32	Nakajima NK1C *Sakae* 21, 1,130 hp	2 × 20 mm 2 × 7.7 mm 2 × 66-lbs or 132-lbs bombs	334 mph at 16,570 feet	7 minutes 19 seconds 19,685 feet	36,250 feet	1,485 miles max
A6M3	22	Nakajima NK1C *Sakae* 21, 1,130 hp	2 × 20 mm 2 × 7.7 mm 2 × 66-lbs or 132-lbs bombs	332 mph at 16,570 feet	about 4,500 feet per minute	36,250 feet	1,400+ miles max
A6M2-K		Nakajima NK1C *Sakae* 12, 950 hp	2 × 7.7 mm	296 mph at 13,120 feet	7 minutes 56 seconds to 19,685 ft	33,400 feet	800 miles
A6M4		Nakajima *Sakae*					
A6M5	52	Nakijima NK1C *Sakae* 21, 1,130 hp	2 × 20 mm 2 × 7,7 mm	351 mph at 19,685 feet	in excess of 4,500 feet per min	36,000 feet	
A6M5a	52a	Nakajima NK1C *Sakae* 21, 1,130 hp	2 × 20 mm 2 × 7.7 mm	351 mph at 19,685 feet			
A6M5b	52b	Nakajima NK1C *Sakae* 21, 1,130 hp	2 × 20 mm 1 × 7.7 mm 1 × 12.7 mm				
A6M5c	52c	Nakajima *Sakae* 21, 1,130 hp	2 × 20 mm 3 × 12.7 mm 2 × 66-lbs or 132-lbs bombs				
A6M6c	53c	Nakajima *Sakae* 31A, 1,130 hp	2 × 20 mm 3 × 12.7mm	346 mph at 19,685 feet	3,140 feet per min	35,100 feet	1,200 miles +
A6M7	63	Nakajima *Sakae* 31A, 1,130 hp	2 × 20 mm 3 × 12.7mm 1 × 550-lbs bombs				
A6M8c	64	Mitsubishi MK8K *Kinsei* 62, 1,1500 hp	2 × 20 mm 2 × 12.7 mm	355 mph at 19,685 feet	6 minutes 50 seconds to 19,685 ft	36,745 feet	1,200 miles +

Weight Empty	Weight Loaded	Span	Length	Remarks
2,681 lbs	3,763 lbs	36 feet 1 inch	29 feet 9½ inches	
3,642 lbs	5,140 lbs	39 feet 4 7/16 inches		First flew 1st April 1939
3,704 lbs	5,313 lbs	39 feet 4 7/16 inches	29 feet 8 11/16 inches	Folding wingtips for carrier operations. Ailerons improved.
3,704 lbs	5,313 lbs	39 feet 4 7/16 inches	29 feet 8 11/16 inches	First production variant
4,235 lbs	6,349 lbs	39 feet 4 7/16 inches	33 feet 1 5/8 inches	Floatplane version. Length measured from nose of float to rear of rudder.
3,984 lbs	5,609 lbs	36 feet 1 inch	29 feet 8 11/16 inches	Wingtips clipped and squared off.
4,107 lbs	5,906 lbs	39 feet 4 7/16 inches	29 feet 8 11/16 inches	Full wingtips, including folding mechanism, reinstated.
4,010 lbs	5,792 lbs	39 feet 4 7/16 inches	30 feet ¼ inch	Two-seat trainer.
				Experimental version with turbo-supercharger. Only two built. Basically an A6M2.
	5,753 lbs	36 feet 1 inch	29 feet 8 11/16 inches	Clipped but rounded wingtips. Thrust augmentation from individual exhaust ejector stubs.
		36 feet 1 inch	29 feet 8 11/16 inches	Belt fed cannon. Heavier gauge wing skin giving increased rigidity and higher diving speed.
		36 feet 1 inch	29 feet 8 11/16 inches	First model to possess a heavier fixed armament.
		36 feet 1 inch	29 feet 8 11/16 inches	Designed to incorporate fuel sealing armour, more fuel and better diving speed. Very underpowered.
4,175 lbs	6,047 lbs	36 feet 1 inch	29 feet 8 11/16 inches	Water-methanol fuel injection. Engine very unreliable. Only ninety-three built.
		36 feet 1 inch	29 feet 8 11/16 inches	Designed as a proper bomb-carrying model to supercede the stop-gap Zero models in this role.
4,740 lbs	6,940 lbs	36 feet 1 inch	29 feet 8 11/16 inches	The final Zero version. Climb rate greatly improved.

Bibliography

The Zero Fighter M Okumiya and J Horikoshi (Cassell, London)
Samurai S Sakai (New English Library, London)
Famous Fighters of the Second World War William Green (MacDonald, London)
Japanese Aircraft of the Pacific War R Francillon (G R Putnam, London)